The Severely Disturbed Adolescent

Inpatient, Residential, and Hospital Treatment

The Severely Disturbed Adolescent

Inpatient, Residential, and Hospital Treatment

WILLIAM M. EASSON, M.D.

Medical College of Ohio
Toledo, Ohio

Contents

Preface

Whenever human beings are suffering, the most natural response of those around is to do something—at times to do anything. When adolescents are disturbed or disturbing, the typical reaction is to "treat" and all too often good intentions and bustling activity are equated with supposedly inevitable gain. In recent years, many treatment centers have been developed to provide some form of treatment for these troubled youths. To a casual observer such therapeutically directed investment would seem to guarantee benefit to the young people in these treatment units. This expectation has not been fulfilled: for many disturbed adolescents, an inpatient placement brings not the anticipated emotional growth and personality integration but rather behavioral regression and disruption.

This monograph is a beginning attempt to clarify the very specific indications for hospital treatment and to highlight the type of adolescent disturbance that might be helped in an inpatient therapeutic environment. This consideration of diagnosis and treatment is presented from the standpoint of the intensely active ongoing inpatient process with the adolescent patient. Other vitally important facets of the total treatment process—the treatment interaction with the teenager's parents and family, the diagnostic examination that leads to hospitalization and the essential social-therapeutic interaction with the teenage patient, the hospital and the community beyond the hospital walls—these areas themselves require extensive evaluation and presentation. This volume is written to share, to enrich, and hopefully to stimulate.

Many people have contributed to the production of the final manuscript. To my secretaries, Miss Haugh, Mrs. Jones, and Mrs. Phelps, must go especial thanks for their understanding and perseverance. To my colleagues is due my very sincere gratitude for their continued support. Above all, my appreciation must go to the people who taught me with such consideration and patience—to those young men and young women who so often throughout this book are described impersonally as adolescent "patients"—to them I wish to dedicate this professional Odyssey.

The Severely Disturbed Adolescent

INPATIENT, RESIDENTIAL, AND HOSPITAL TREATMENT

Chapter I

The Prescription of Residential Treatment

Residential treatment is the form of psychiatric therapy that provides the maximum amount of external support and external direction for the disturbed patient. In the inpatient setting, treatment personnel assume the final responsibility for the control of the daily living of another human being. Residential treatment is thus a very specific, most potent treatment modality which is indicated only in certain clearly defined therapeutic circumstances. The injudicious or the ill-timed use of inpatient therapy may not only fail to benefit the patient but may produce irreversible emotional regression and permanent personality stunting. More than any other age group, the growing adolescent is vulnerable and may be handicapped emotionally and intellectually by unnecessary or badly planned hospital placement.

THE HOSPITAL AND THE ADOLESCENT

During adolescence, the growing young man or young woman should become emancipated from the parent-family unit and should evolve a sex-appropriate, goal-directed personal independence. During this phase of "adolescenthood" (Maier, 1965), the teenager must establish and test his own self-controls. He must ascertain and express his own opinions. He must discover his own identity and become individualized from his parents and siblings. The vast majority of teenagers manage this growth task of emancipation with reasonable compe-

1

tence. They struggle and they suffer but, by and large, they cope and they mature. While considerable diagnostic and treatment emphasis has been focused on the anxieties of adolescent development (Masterson, 1967), it can be suggested that the emotional turmoil of adolescence is no greater, and perhaps no more distressing, than the individual stress and the personality dysfunction seen at other comparable developmental, transitional stages in human individual and cultural growth. Many of the symptomatic expressions of adolescent anxiety and teenage discomfort are similar to the emotional reaction patterns seen during the menopause and the senium when again the human organism undergoes profound physiological, anatomical, and emotional changes and where the changing person has to adapt to a new role in his family and in his society. Recent authors (Grinker, 1962; Offer, Sabshin and Marcus, 1965; Masterson and Washburne, 1966) highlight not only the pain and anxiety of the sensitive, normal adolescent but also the reality that the vast majority of teenagers do cope successfully with the developmental and the emancipatory tasks of adolescence.

As the adolescent separates emotionally and becomes independent of his parents and his family, the personal ego anxiety he feels as a result of this separation serves as a profound continued stimulus to his rapid emotional and intellectual growth. When the teenager has to stand on his own two feet emotionally and is obliged to formulate his opinions and his hopes, he becomes acutely aware that he is not fully adequate and not completely competent. Under the goad of what he feels to be his own inadequacies, the coping adolescent is stimulated to experiment further, to master, to learn and to grow. During this phase of emotional development, the adolescent is not necessarily comfortable, unanxious, or completely happy but he is maturing and, to a major extent, managing reasonably well. While he does have difficulties in controlling his heightened inner impulses, the coping adolescent usually is able to contain and to direct these energies. While he struggles under the pressure of society's demands and of his own expectations, he is usually able to tolerate this emotional tension and to work out a solution acceptable both to himself and to those around him.

This adolescent growth-emancipation task is dependent on the teenager's inherent ego strength and capabilities, on his ability to acquire strength and support through relating to his family, his peers, and his culture, and on the internal and external stresses with which he has to cope. If the growing adolescent cannot constructively use the impulses, the energies, and the strivings of adolescence toward further emotional development and increasing personality capability, these unchanneled, uncontrolled forces will cause mounting personality disruption. The personal gratification brought by increasing mastery and self-sufficiency greatly strengthens the teenager's capability for further development. If the adolescent cannot use his inner drives toward further maturation and greater mastery, he will begin to miss the growth pleasure and the ego gratification that come with increasing ability. His resultant natural anger and frustration will mount, will be turned in on himself, and will cause spiraling personality disruption. If the adolescent is faced with emotional and intellectual demands beyond his strength, his personality growth may slow and he may use an increasing number of maladaptive "sick" emotional defenses. When the teenager's emotional resources are overwhelmed by the stresses and the demands of the adolescent responsibilities, he may cease completely in his emotional growth and may even show retrogression in personality development. His maladaptive defenses, activated by the pressure of his mounting anxiety, may lead to behavior that further undermines his emotional and social development. At some point in this disruptive process, it may be asked whether residential treatment is necessary for this disturbed and disturbing teenager.

While leaders of psychiatric opinion (Felix, 1961; Gilbert, 1965; Warren, 1965b) are indicating that additional residential treatment facilities for disturbed adolescents are required, they do not mention specific criteria for hospitalization in any such units. Recent monographs (Holmes, 1964; Miller, 1964) give little indication of the kind of adolescent patient the authors see as benefiting from their treatment facilities. Beckett (1965) mentions that adolescents are usually referred for inpatient treatment because they show behavior that "adult society considers boisterous, aggressive or violent." Under these criteria alone, most teenagers at some time during their emotional growth would qualify for residential treatment. The indications for admission to the inpatient setting must be clearly understood. For hospital treatment to be effective and beneficial, the adolescent must require and be able to use this specific hospitalization experience.

DIAGNOSIS FOR INPATIENT TREATMENT

When the teenager lacks the individual ego strength to cope with his inner impulses but is emotionally capable of utilizing the bond of meaningful relationships and the support of environmental structuring, he can usually use his relationship capability to compensate reasonably well for his ego weaknesses. Thus he can use his friends and his family to provide him with controls and with direction. Emotionally he can lean on his siblings, his peers, and his companions until he develops sufficient additional personal ego strength to stand erect and self-sufficient. If he has the ability to form meaningful continued relationships, he can use the rules and the customs of his culture and the explicit laws of his community to provide himself with personal guidelines. If he has an ability to relate meaningfully, he may also be able to use an outpatient psychotherapy process in a growth-producing fashion, with the support of his family and his environment. The adolescent does not require inpatient treatment when he has the capability of using the strength of relationships to continue functioning as a member of society.

If the unsettled adolescent has sufficient personal strength to handle his inner impulses and to use his adolescent energy toward further mastery experience and growth, he should be able to maintain himself outside a hospital treatment setting, even though he may lack the emotional capability to form meaningful permanent relationships. With his inherent ego strengths, such an adolescent can profit from experience and can be conditioned psychologically. With his mastery ability, this teenager will be able to face reality problems and acquire knowledge. Though the young patient may be totally narcissistically oriented, he may have sufficient ego capability to continue growing emotionally within his limitations. The training and the direction he needs may be better given him in a school system or in a specifically planned training institution. A closely supportive hospital placement would tend to undermine his basic ego strengths by providing personal controls where controls are not required.

Where the disturbed adolescent is lacking both in ego strength to handle his inner drives and in the ability to form meaningful, stable relationships, most likely he will require continued inpatient treatment. Where he is wanting both in self-control and in relationship capability, he may not have the emotional ability to seek or to use external ego strengthening to compensate for his personality weaknesses. Until he can develop sufficient ego strength, this adolescent may require inpatient treatment to give him adequate external ego strengthening and to insure that the continued demands of adolescence do not cause personal tensions that will disrupt his further growth. Before it is decided that inpatient treatment is the appropriate therapeutic approach for a disturbed adolescent, two basic criteria should both be present—

1. From the examination process it should be clearly demonstrated that the disturbed teenager lacks sufficient personal strength to control his own drives and impulses. It should be shown that he is unable to use his surging adolescent energy toward mastery and growth and that he can neither harness nor channel these drives. A profound deficit in ego strength should be present before hospitalization is considered.

2. During the diagnostic evaluation, it should be shown that the teenager lacks the emotional capability necessary to form sufficiently strong, meaningful relationships with people in his family and his culture so that

he can use the continued strength and the direction of such relationships to give him adequate self-control and self-direction. A profound deficit in relationship capability should be demonstrated before hospitalization is prescribed.

A diagnostic examination prior to inpatient hospitalization should demonstrate that the sick teenager does not have the emotional capability to complement his own emotional resources by the usual social, educational, and family forms of external ego strengthening. In such a treatment situation, the massive ego support and direction provided by a residential treatment center may then be the therapeutic program needed.

The disturbed adolescent may require residential therapy due to many underlying etiological factors; the criteria for inpatient admission do not specify any particular cause. The treatment approach in the residential setting must be planned with due understanding for the individual needs of each teenage patient.

Where the emotional status of the disturbed teenager does not meet these two diagnostic criteria but he is still placed in an inpatient treatment setting, the therapeutic results may be disastrous for the adolescent and for the treatment unit. In those areas where the emancipating adolescent does not require the massive external ego strengthening provided by a residential milieu, residential treatment will tend to crush his nascent individuality. Where the adolescent is capable of forming strong, meaningful relationships and of utilizing environmental direction and structure productively, the firm, external imposition of such structuring as occurs in the residential setting will act directly counter to the adolescent emancipation-individuation process. Ill-advised residential placement may cause iatrogenic illness and even produce permanent emotional handicapping.

Inpatient treatment is sometimes recommended as a necessary measure to separate the emotionally ill adolescent from a disturbed family environment (Mechanick and Nathan, 1965). If the disturbed adolescent does have the ability, even partially, to control and to channel his impulses, or if he is capable of using meaningful relationships to provide him with emotional support, his separation from a disruptive family environment will lead to greater emotional growth if he is placed in a boarding home, an appropriate school, an apartment, or in a home with friends or relatives. In these more normal social settings, the environmental expectations for continued adolescent maturation would be maintained. The anxiety of the separation experience would stimulate this adolescent to develop his limited ego resources. With his relationship ability, such a teenager is able to reach out to those around him and with his inherent ego strength he can muster his personal emotional capabilities to struggle further and to grow. The moderately competent adolescent will be able to use a separation experience as an ego growth task. In a residential setting, the all-encompassing environmental support minimizes this separation shock. For the coping adolescent, such unnecessary support removes the necessary growth impetus of separation. The massive ego strengthening provided by the inpatient treatment unit not only neutralizes the loss of family support but minimizes the need for emancipation. At the adolescent growth stage when the teenager separates from his family and begins to depend largely on his own personality resources, he is extremely vulnerable to a regressive emotional pull; residential placement at this time may cause and perpetuate emotional dependence. Thus, for the reasonably coping adolescent, separation from a disturbed family situation into a residential treatment unit may be an emotionally stunting experience.

Residential placement has been suggested for its "punishment" effect (Sobel, 1953; Alt, 1960). Punishment and residential treatment are almost directly contradictory in treatment purpose. Meaningful punishment, to be emotionally productive, must cause personal anxiety which leads to emotional change and personality growth. If the disturbed adolescent is so lacking in individual ego strength that he does in fact require residential treatment, by definition he also lacks the ego capability to profit by a meaningful punishment experience. If he is so deficient in personal ego strengths and in relationship capabilities that he requires inpatient treatment, the emotional pain and the anxiety caused by punishment will further over- whelm his minimal emotional resources (Alderton, 1967). If the disturbed adolescent has sufficient personality strengths and relationship capabilities so that punishment can be used as a meaningful growth experience, a residential placement would be an ego-stunting treatment approach for such a teen- ager. For this more competent young man or young woman there are many punitive social and legal agencies available and offering punishment at all levels of treatment sophistication or barbarity—boarding schools, military academies, reform schools, prisons and penitentiaries—all are planned to arouse enough personal anxiety in the adolescent that he will change and grow. For the teenager who is channeling his adolescent energy and his meaningful relationship capabilities, these in- stitutions and these agencies provide various levels of poten- tially growth-producing punishment experiences.

Too frequently, however, adolescents are still placed in resi- dential settings "to bring them to their senses." Too often, well-intentioned parents prefer to place the antisocial adoles- cent in their family in a residential treatment unit rather than to help him face the consequences and the responsibilities of his socially unproductive behavior. Though such placement may temporarily remove the threat of social disgrace or of se- vere legal retribution, the placement of an otherwise emotion- ally competent adolescent in a treatment institution, for the purposes of punishment under the guise of treatment, may pro- duce profound permanent emotional crippling.

Harry was a 17 year old high school senior from a socially comfortable, middle-class family environment. He was doing well in school academi- cally and was popular with his peer group. One evening Harry, with a group of boys and girls from his high school class, went out on a drinking spree. While these teenagers were drunk, they took part in group sexual activities, colloquially known as a "gang bang." This was Harry's first heterosexual experience.

On the day after this incident, the parents of one girl involved complained to the local police. When they were contacted by the police, Harry's parents were horrified. They anticipated that their name and his name would be dragged through the local papers, with their son portrayed as a rapist. In their anxiety they saw his future academic career shattered by any legal action. They were also furious with their son whom they felt had let them down badly. After a discussion with the local physician, it was decided that Harry must be "sick." His parents felt also that he should be "made to think." So that he might have treatment for his "sickness" and to stimulate his "thinking," Harry was placed in a residential treatment unit. His antisocial behavior was interpreted to the treatment team as most certainly being due to profound emotional illness.

This 17 year old young man was at first bitterly ashamed about his behavior and the publicity with which he was now faced. He was bewildered at his hospital placement but, when his bewilderment began to clear, he remained infuriated by the residential controls. He felt that the ward regulations were a totally unnecessary infantilization which he regarded as having to be fought in order to maintain his very self-respect. Quickly Harry and the treatment staff members found themselves at loggerheads. The therapeutic team resolutely demanded that Harry be placed in the closed residential ward for the most disturbed, disorganized patients.

In this instance, further punishment was being sought under the guise of necessary "treatment." Regression was being demanded as a therapeutic measure. Only with calmer consideration could it be clarified that placement in a residential treatment unit was totally inappropriate for this young man. He felt guilty and reasonably ashamed about his behavior. He required punishment in order to continue satisfactory emotional growth. The appropriate anger and the shame he should have been directing toward himself was being vented on the hospital staff who had set themselves up as most appropriate targets for his anger. This personal anger and shame could be more beneficially used by this young man to produce inner emotional shifts and eventually greater maturity.

From a consideration of his background history and from his diagnostic examination, it could be clearly shown that this teenager had successfully begun his emancipation from his family and was channeling his drives and his impulses with moderate efficiency in his everyday living. At his age-appropriate level of ego competency, he was capable of using a shame and punishment experience toward meaningful, integrated ego growth. When he was placed in a hospital environment, the externally applied ego supports tended to force a dependent

9

relationship and to produce an emotional regression. To maintain his newly won independence and the ego growth he had established during adolescence, this young man had no option but to fight the external supports and the direction imposed by the inpatient setting. If he had allowed himself to become a "patient," he would have surrendered independence already achieved and would have given up self-control already established. If a teenager is admitted to an inpatient setting largely for punishment purposes, so much of his emotional energy becomes involved in fighting to maintain his independence and self-direction, that little is left for growth toward further ego maturity. If such a wrongfully prescribed course of inpatient treatment is maintained, the drives and the energies of the adolescent become largely invested in fighting hospital-enforced regression. Iatrogenic delay of further personality maturation and a possibly permanent stunting of emotional growth may be produced.

If a teenager is placed in a residential treatment unit largely because his ideas and his opinions are counter to those of his family or his society, this residential treatment program is being used to crush individuality and to counteract independence—against the natural growth process. If residential placement is used to force the teenager back into a parental pattern, the treatment facility is working contrary to the natural adolescent emancipation. If the teenager has sufficient ego strength to handle his inner anxieties and to use his drives toward emancipation, he has the personal capability to use the training and the control provided by normally available social agencies such as schools, churches, adolescent peer organizations, and legal agencies. It is not the therapeutic function of a residential treatment program to force the ideas of parents and of society on the emancipating adolescent. Psychiatric assistance may help the teenager to utilize his potential as fully as possible, and to make the optimum adaptation to the reality of his environment. Residential treatment centers must not accept adolescent patients for "treatment" merely because the adolescent boy or girl has decided to marry, to leave school or to move away from home against the parental wishes. If these anxiety-arousing decisions are based on the realistic thinking of a coping adolescent, such decisions may produce necessary growth experiences which should not be counteracted by a residential placement. Only where such behavior is part of a pattern of disorganized, disruptive, or infantile reactions by an adolescent who cannot handle his tensions and who cannot face the reasonable expectations of society, only then should residential placement be considered as one possible means of providing external strength and direction which may be required for that teenager at that time.

When a disturbing adolescent is placed in a residential unit largely to bring him under some form of external control, the therapeutic results may be disastrous both for the teenager and for the treating team.

At age 16, Bill was placed in a residential treatment unit because he was "beyond parental control." This otherwise competent young man wished to be an auto mechanic, for which occupation he was well qualified, but his financially very successful father wished him to enter the family business. By the time of his hospital admission, the family arguments about Bill's future career had raised tensions to an unbearable point. Bill's parents felt that he was "unliveable" and "irrational." His opinions of his parents were totally unprintable.

At the time of his hospitalization, Bill could see absolutely no reason why he should "submit" to the staff controls provided by the residential center or why he should accept the external direction of the treatment personnel. Very soon he stated loudly and bluntly that he had "a mind of his own." He refused to conform to the hospital regulations so that rapidly the treatment team and this young man were locked in a battle to see who could control him. To an increasingly untherapeutic degree, the energy of the entire treatment team, the hospital unit, and this young man himself, was caught up in this struggle. Other adolescent patients became involved in this conflict so that angers and tensions within the treatment unit spiraled. Eventually, because his totally uncooperative behavior was held to be due to an underlying psychotic process still not clearly elucidated, this young man was given a course of 10 electroshock treatments. Following this series of convulsive therapy, the young man was moderately confused and slightly less defiant. The treatment personnel, however, felt much better.

11

Only with more rational consideration could it be admitted that the defiance of this adolescent boy was largely engendered by his need to protect his uncertain independence. His wish to remain unshackled by the hospital controls was based on his struggles to remain emancipated. The optimum therapeutic role of the caring team should have been to strengthen his maturation drive and to stabilize his self-controls. Prior to this hospital admission, Bill had managed quite competently in a wide social and academic sphere outside his home. If he had been retained in a hospital setting where external ego supports and direction were provided whether he needed it or not, an emotional illness would have been produced rather than treated.

Inpatient treatment is one of the most powerful tools in the psychiatric armamentarium. Since hospital treatment provides the maximum external ego support and direction with the minimum necessary patient cooperation, this treatment procedure must be directed specifically toward those adolescents who lack both the ego strength to control their own tensions and the relationship capability to compensate for their weaknesses. Where a disturbed adolescent meets these two basic criteria, inpatient treatment may be the therapeutic procedure of choice and may be necessary for his continued growth.

Chapter II

The Therapeutic Facilities of a Residential Unit for Disturbed Adolescents

In planning an adolescent treatment unit, the residential team must consider exactly what the treatment personnel and the adolescent patients can do and should be expected to do with the treatment facilities available to them. An adolescent treatment unit, situated on the sixth floor of a general hospital, will have a markedly different treatment program and purpose than a treatment unit located on a country farm. In considering the patients they wish to help, treatment staff must clarify in their own minds precisely what they mean by "adolescent" or "teenager." In Western culture, a 13 year old is a teenager, a 16 year old is a teenager, and a 19 year old is considered a teenager but, in normal adolescent society, each age level has vitally different interests, capabilities, and goals. In the junior high school, at 13 years of age, the growing adolescent naturally moves with his peer group and normally mirrors the customs of this "crowd." Thirteen, 14 and even 15 year old teenagers tend to look alike in appearance and to act similarly. These young adolescents function to a large extent in the role as members of a group, a gang, or a clique. The teenager in high school in his natural growth process is beginning to emancipate from his peer group and is forming more individualized friendships and interests with both boys and girls. Though the 16 year old teenager still moves with his gang or social group, he has the emotional freedom and flexibility to be independent of this group. Any environmental or social pressure to push the 16 year old exclusively toward group activities would be forcing a form of behavior which is emotionally regressive at this stage of adolescent growth. By 19 years of age, young men and women, though still called adolescents, are now considered by society and by their peers to be almost adults. At this age level, these teenagers form close one-to-one relationships which may endure throughout their lives. They marry and they have children. Their culture judges them emotionally capable of bearing arms and of dying for their country. In normal society it is not considered possible to establish any kind of program which would adequately meet the interests of the whole adolescent age group. In the public school setting, these teenagers are sepparated into natural groups comprising junior high school, high school, and college. Thus during this period these teenagers are children, adults, and parents despite the fact that they are all adolescents and they are all regarded as teenagers.

While it is considered unreasonable if not impossible to set up one specific educational, recreational, or vocational program that will interest teenagers at all levels of adolescent development, it is even less possible to establish a residential treatment program for all adolescent age levels between 13 and 19 within the one adolescent unit. Disturbed adolescents show within the age span of adolescence an even wider range of emotional reactions and personal capabilities than their age peers. Two disturbed teenagers may be of exactly the same age and physical capability and may test psychologically at a comparable level intellectually, but they may differ drastically in their emotional interests and social capabilities. The psychotic youth may be outstanding in his comprehension of electronics yet may be totally incapable of understanding a simple basketball game. The socially disruptive, acting-out teenager may be an expert on the football field yet totally unaware of even the basic essentials of simple scientific knowledge. Two disturbed adolescents

14

of the same age, same sex, and similar physical capability may be diagnosed with identical diagnostic labels and yet have grossly different emotional handicaps. The psychotic adolescent who is basically autistic, may be adept athletically but grossly retarded intellectually and socially; his inability to relate may make it impossible for him to take part in any team sports since he is insensitive to team interactions. Another psychotic adolescent, who shows a schizophrenic pattern, may be so sensitive to his own inner struggles and to the feelings of other people that he is totally incapable of facing the aggressive competitive aspects of team sports. The treatment approach to these two adolescents, both diagnosed as psychotic and both incapable of engaging in team athletic activities at that moment, should be very different. No one treatment program can deal therapeutically in the same unit with all adolescent age levels or with all levels of ego dysfunction seen in the disturbed teenager. If the resources of a treatment program are directed in too many different areas, all therapeutic benefits may be dissipated; the treatment staff are liable to become confused, anxious, and frustrated if the therapeutic program appears to lack integration and consistency.

The disturbed adolescent must be treated both as an individual and as part of an appropriate peer group. Konopka (1955, 1961) emphasizes how group associations support personal individuality and self-acceptance. Where such group acceptance is not readily available, the teenage patient finds it more difficult to develop his own secure self-confidence and self-control; without group support and direction he is more likely to act disruptively (Warren, 1952). Many disturbed adolescents can use their social groups as a source of external strength, as a safer group for initial trusting relationships, and as a source of early identification models. As the uncertain teenager essays his first steps toward emotional emancipation, the support and the direction of an empathic understanding group is essential for his emotional stability. In any meaningful treatment process for disturbed adolescents, the treating team must work actively with the adolescent on his own and in his role as member of a group.

As Beskind (1962) points out in his review, several authors recommend that adolescents and especially older adolescents, should be cared for in adult treatment units. It is suggested that this mixing of disturbed teenagers with older patients brings greater control to the adolescent patient group. In many instances this adolescent patient dilution seems to be dictated more by the needs of the treating staff than by the emotional requirements of the teenagers. With no other patients, do therapeutic personnel in this fashion seriously suggest that other sick, disturbed patients be used as final identification models for the emotionally developing individual. Where teenagers share the same treatment unit as older patients, too often the adult and the adolescent patient groups act out their illnesses and anxieties for each other in a most unproductive fashion. The younger, less experienced adolescent may become the hapless focus for the aggressive and the sexualized drives of the uncontrolled adult patient. A long-time adult male patient described the kind of homosexual attack to which a teenager may be exposed in a comparatively unsupervised adult-adolescent unit.

> The men are always on the lookout for some kid who is young and innocent. They catch him the night he comes in. Sometimes I feel that the attendant goes along with the whole thing. Some of those aides seem pretty ready for a piece themselves. The men wait until the boy is in bed. They usually give him the corner bed. Then, when no one is around, they jump him. They use a blanket to keep him down and to keep him quiet. These men have been in hospital so long that they will use anything with a hole.

The inadequate adolescent who is unable to control his feelings can be taught illness by adult patients. The uncertain teenager who lacks confidence can have his self-esteem further undermined by disturbed adults. In a group therapy session a middle-aged woman patient related:

> These teenagers put on a show and pretend they know a lot. Most of them don't know beans. They come in, they prance around and they

16

make a lot of noise but they are really ignorant. It is fun to teach them the facts of life.

If teenage patients are placed in adult units, they are too often taught the "facts of life," both healthy and unhealthy. In a fashion that does not promote teenage emotional growth, the older patients tend to use the younger adolescent to act out aggressive angry impulses. Since the adult patient does not have complete self-trust and self-confidence, he cannot give the adolescent the relationship experience of being fully trusted by a stable person. With only slight prompting and subtle encouragement, the impressionable adolescent may be prompted to disruptive behavior that not only disorganizes the environment but also disrupts the teenager's own emotional and intellectual growth. The older adult patient may be sitting quietly watching while the teenagers he aroused are causing disruption and tumult amongst the staff and the patient group.

The energetic, activity-oriented adolescent, whose impulses and drives are so near the surface emotionally, is a disruptive force to adult patients who are trying to achieve their own self-control and self-understanding. The uncontrolled behavior of an adolescent patient may shatter the laboriously erected compulsive defenses of the emotionally fragile adult. Where the uncertain adult patient makes his anxieties bearable through a process of emotional denial, this necessary defense may crumble catastrophically in face of the primitive expressiveness of teenage patients on the same treatment unit. Where adult patients are striving to establish personal stability and security, the emotional fluidity and the energy of an adolescent group too often is a source of disruption in a potentially productive treatment process for adults.

Growth oriented programs must be planned for specific treatment groups of adolescent patients. While the activity oriented disturbed adolescent may require maximal environmental control and support, he also needs opportunities to sublimate his high level of tension in more productive activities. He must be able to channel his aggression through hard physical activity, through individual sports, and eventually through strenuous team athletic interactions. The action oriented teenager may well begin a school program in the wood shop or in the auto mechanics unit long before he is able to tolerate the relative inactivity of the academically oriented history or mathematics class. For the withdrawn psychotic teenager, environmental intrusion may be more necessary than direct control and support. In the residential unit and in the school program, the treatment team members must reach into the autistic world of the adolescent and form some bond of common interest so that gradually he can be drawn out into the wider social environment. In the treatment setting, the infantile, immature teenager must have the opportunity to be himself, to be openly childlike in a fashion which does not shame him. In his treatment program, it may be necessary for the caring personnel to relate to him first at his very self-centered narcissistic level so that, based on this narcissistic bond, the childlike adolescent can be gradually encouraged and supported to find gratification in people and things outside himself. For each treatment approach, different therapeutic facilities are necessary. For the changing growth and developmental stages of adolescence and for the very wide range of emotional disorders seen within this age group, a wide spectrum of therapeutic facilities is necessary. Since no treatment unit and no therapeutic staff can undertake to treat every facet of emotional illness, the teenage patient must be carefully selected for admission according to the treatment facilities of the specific treatment unit, the therapeutic capabilities of the caring personnel and the composition of the resident patient group.

THE TREATMENT PURPOSE OF THE RESIDENTIAL FACILITIES

Every facet of the inpatient unit must be geared to enhance the emotional strengths and capabilities of the disturbed teenager and to produce personality growth. All aspects of residential living must be directed toward supporting whatever individual ego strengths the teenage patient has and toward promoting whatever relationship capability he possesses. While the purpose of inpatient treatment is to promote increased self-confidence and personal stability in the adolescent, the treatment team must face the reality that the first effect of hospital admission is to further undermine the teenager's emotional competence.

The experience of the personal psychiatric examination and the diagnosis of emotional illness is a severe blow to the teenager's individual self-confidence. Just as he is supposed to emancipate, to become independent and to live according to his own strengths and capabilities, by virtue of the psychiatric diagnosis he is judged to be not fully capable. In the eyes of his family, his culture, and most important in his own eyes, he is considered to be lacking in sufficient personality strengths to direct and control his own living. He is diagnosed as incapable, weak and, frequently "bad." While a definite psychiatric examination and a specific diagnosis are essential before any meaningful treatment program can begin, it must be clearly appreciated that such a diagnostic procedure initially further undermines the uncertain personality strengths of the disturbed adolescent. In their very private peer discussions, and sometimes during the course of psychotherapy, hospitalized adolescents will talk with much personal agony about the anguish, the fear, and the shame brought about by this label of psychiatric illness.

> They think we are animals in a zoo. Folks outside figure that we swing from chandeliers like monkeys. I know what they are thinking as soon as they guess I'm from this place—they think I'm a babbling idiot. My folks thought I was crazy—they had to get rid of me because they couldn't stand me!

Many procedures at the time of hospital admission and during the course of inpatient treatment tend further to undermine the self-confidence and the personality strength of the adolescent patient and patients at all age levels (Zusman, 1967). When they are first admitted to the hospital, many disturbed adolescents are potentially assaultive or suicidal so it may be necessary to search them thoroughly. While such searches are essential from one aspect of the treatment process, it must be appreciated that, to any self-respecting adolescent, this "frisking" is an embarrassing, disrespectful, personal intrusion. Many treatment units with limited financial resources must insist that the adolescent patient live with little personal privacy in a room or dormitory furnished with institutional monotony. Because of insufficient housekeeping or laundry staff, the teenager's desire for personalized bedding, for individualized room decoration, or for different clothing may be rejected completely by the hospital administration. In planning a treatment program, it must be appreciated what emotional price the teenager pays in this further undermining of his personal confidence and stability as he becomes integrated in an institutional program. In large treatment institutions which are poorly supported financially, one comparatively untrained attendant may care for many teenagers. No matter how sensitive such an aide or child care worker may be, he will have little time to encourage or to support the individuality of the different teenagers. So that the total institution runs with minimum tension and with maximum efficiency, it may be necessary for the hard pressed staff to insist on conformity, even at the price of individuality and personal capability. All psychiatric patients are harmed by such a treatment approach but the emancipating adolescent is especially injured. In any useful treatment program, the individual strength he has should be supported and encouraged so that he can grow to become self-controlling and self-supporting.

Many understaffed, poorly financed, inadequately directed treatment institutions for teenagers make extensive use of seclusion rooms and heavy blanketing dosages of tranquilizing drugs. While such a treatment approach might be beneficial in certain very select instances, a general use of repressive, controlling measures will produce emotional crippling rather than appropriate adolescent growth. The teenager must learn to develop his own strengths and his own capacity to relate to people. If he is constantly doped with tranquilizing medications, he may be more bearable to those around him and thus have a somewhat greater opportunity to relate directly to people. On the other hand, it is also possible that he may be living almost exclusively in his own shadowy world, bemused by drugs. Medication should never be used to shut off the adolescent from those around him because such a treatment approach may cause cessation of relationship growth and may lead to permanent stunting of personality maturation. While it is absolutely essential that the disturbed adolescent be given suitable external controls, where he lacks inner controls for his impulses and drives, these supports should be human-based controls. The growing young man must be taught and supported to develop his own human controls. Such teaching-treatment can only be given through meaningful interaction with other human beings. If the uncontrolled adolescent is controlled solely through incarceration in a seclusion room, he learns to relate only to four bare walls but not to people. In a locked room by himself he is given no human examples that he can internalize and no emotional rewards to stimulate further self-control. Where he is already uncertain of his relationship capability, sustained imprisonment in a seclusion room further undermines such relationship. He learns there only to relate to himself in an autistic, narcissistic or psychopathic fashion—in a seclusion room he can talk only to himself, he can hold only his own hand, he can test his dreams and his hopes only against his own ideas. The use of primitive physical restraints or of seclusion rooms in a treatment setting will tend to perpetuate emotional crippling in the adolescent and to produce adults who will be unproductive and a burden to society. In the long run, such an institutionally directed treatment approach is far more costly financially and socially than an individually oriented treatment setting which makes use of extensive and expensive people power.

Every facet of living in a good treatment unit should be geared toward enhancing the teenager's relationship capability. In many poorly staffed treatment centers, there are insufficient therapeutic team members to interact with the adolescents. These teenage patients are encouraged and, at times, forced to spend a large part of their day watching the tranquilizing television box. An adolescent sitting in front of the little screen day after day, is taught to relate to moving, mechanical figures on this screen but not to human beings around him. His relationship capability becomes stunted and, in many instances, permanently undermined by this emphasis on the use of television. During adolescence, the teenager naturally has to learn his own patterns of relating with people. At this time he begins to finalize his patterns of reaction to those around him and to develop his adult social sensitivities. With his limited emotional resources, the disturbed adolescent is especially vulnerable to any treatment approach which limits his meaningful interactions.

At this stage in his personality growth, the adolescent is particularly susceptible to the emotionally handicapping, institutionalizing effects of deadening impersonal controls; such mechanical, nonhuman controls accentuate a natural adolescent tendency to emotional withdrawal and to the use of autistic or narcissistic defenses. If the teenager's early relationships have been painful and disturbing, a period of only weeks or months of enforced isolation or of limitation from warm human relationships may irrevocably fix this developing adolescent in a narcissistic, institutionalized pattern of relating. As he gropingly tries to relate to himself and to those around him, the controlling ego-strengthening experiences of a useful treatment program must be provided by human beings. Most authors, who consider the treatment needs of teenagers in the inpatient setting, emphasize the need for controls but it must be pointed out strongly that these controls have to be human-based controls and strengths (Warren, 1952; Dettelbach, 1955; Redl and Wineman, 1957, p. 446; Miller, 1957; Hendrickson and Holmes, 1959; Stahl, 1960; and many others). As Bettelheim and Sylvester (1948) point out, the treatment team in an adolescent unit must constantly intrude into the world of the disturbed teenager as he is able to tolerate such intrusions. The provision of both the external ego supports and the continued available human relationships for these adolescent patients requires a very high staff-patient ratio. Unless a treatment unit is able to provide both this high staff ratio and the quality of staff personnel emotionally capable of supporting and relating to these adolescents, treatment of the disturbed adolescent should not be attempted.

The therapeutic use of the teenager's daily living in the residential unit is the main treatment tool in inpatient therapy. Not only should wide use be made of "life space interviews" (Redl and Wineman, 1957) but through ordinary, simple daily living interactions, the adolescent patient should have a constant meaningful growth and relationship experience (Noshpitz, 1962). As the teenage girl cooks and tidies with the child care worker, she learns not only the pleasures of personal organization and the gratification of work accomplished but also the warmth of doing things comfortably together. When he plays pool with the staff member, the teenage boy learns how to control his aggression and how to use this forcefulness in a competitive growth-producing fashion. He discovers that he can compete and succeed without destroying; he learns he can lose without being annihilated. Eventually, by repeated living experiences, he discovers that he can have pleasure in the success of someone for whom he cares, even at the price of his own defeat. In the swimming pool, the anxious adolescent learns to trust himself in an uncertain environment when he is sure that staff members will come to his support if he needs such support. The adolescent girl, fearful and uncertain of her own body image, finds that she is not damaged and not engulfed when the child-care worker puts her hair up in curlers. If a residential center is to provide treatment geared for emotional growth and personal self-sufficiency rather than custodial incarceration, such a treatment unit must have facilities and staff adequate to promote the individuality of each adolescent patient and to give the individual teenager sufficient opportunity for growth toward independence, sublimation, and mature relationships. As these disturbed adolescents gradually learn to relate to their environment, they may first direct their emotions toward things or toward animals. In a meaningful treatment program, these relationship growth possibilities must be available and the treatment team has to be aware of the benefits and the drawbacks of such individualized treatment opportunities.

The introduction of a pet into an adolescent treatment unit may bring many individual and group benefits but also causes many anxieties. Though a pet may belong to one specific teenager, invariably all members of the adolescent group react positively or negatively to its presence. Even though one adolescent boy has a single goldfish hidden away in his room, the whole residential group will be aware of the presence of this living creature. The treatment team thus deals not only with the reaction of one teenager to his personal pet but also with the response of the whole treatment group, both staff and patient, to this interaction going on between the one teenager and the one fish. If this fish should mysteriously die, not only will the treatment team have to deal with the reaction of the owner of the fish but also with the response of the other teenage patients on the unit. When a psychotic adolescent, in a moment of uncontrolled passion, killed his pet goldfish with thumbtacks, his primitive murderous behavior caused so much staff and patient anxiety that he was rejected and isolated for months.

Hamsters make for active, energetic, interesting pets. They can be contained in a small cage in a small room. Before a teenager is allowed to acquire a hamster as a pet, the treatment team must be very much aware that hamsters, if handled too much, will tend to eat their young. While some disturbed adolescents will deliberately produce such cannibalism in their pet hamsters, others will promote such behavior inadvertently—if a hamster mother does happen to eat her newborn infants, her behavior is liable to produce a very strong reaction in any treatment unit. For many teenage patients, such murderous behavior too much reflects their past home environment. Ham-

24

sters and guinea pigs may be pleasant to play with but have the unfortunate habit of developing fatal asthmatic spasms if handled too roughly. Many adolescent inpatients have discovered that in the past their awkward protestations of love and affection brought forth only anger and rejection from the meaningful people in their environment. If their loving roughness leads to the death of a pet, this repetition of past experience may cause explosive emotional turmoil. Though larger pets may be the legal property of one patient, in reality they are the emotional property of the whole treatment group. If a cat or a dog is not tolerated by each individual member of the residential group, this pet may become the unfortunate object of primitive feelings. Unless the pet is big enough to care for itself and to protect itself, it may become the focus of anger directed toward its owner or toward other people who care for the pet. If a pet is blinded or maimed, its presence on the treatment unit may be a persistent source of group anxiety; to send an injured animal away might echo too much of the kind of rejection these adolescents have had in the past. The presence of animals on a treatment unit may bring many therapeutic benefits but such a treatment approach must be carefully worked through with the adolescent group and with the total treatment team. If pets can be tolerated, frequently it is easier for the uncertain teenager to relate first to an animal before he takes the risk of relating to people. The infantile-immature adolescent may first love a cat because it is soft and silky. As the psychotic teenager gropes toward people, he may first hug the affectionate dog in preference to an unresponsive pillow.

Where the adolescent is too insecure to relate to animals or to people, he may first care for a plant. The adolescent who does not know how to love human beings may first love a seed which he tends until it flowers. The teenage girl who is not yet able to love a person or to cherish an animal, may nurture a plant with maternal devotion. Even plants can become the focus for disturbing illness. A child-care worker wrote in his daily report.

Charley spent three hours playing with "Mother" tonight. Since he started calling his Venus's-flytrap this name, he has tended to spend every evening in his room with his plant. The other boys tell me that he traps ants and feeds them to the plant. They say he spends hours just watching these plants eat the ants. He loves to see the insects squirm as they are trapped and eaten.

Though this psychotic adolescent could relate only to this carnivorous plant, he was showing a beginning ability to relate to some thing outside himself. In a good residential treatment setting, this very limited relationship ability should be supported even at so disturbed a level; gradually and very tentatively the treatment staff should try to widen the area of the adolescent patient's relationships. If the very disturbed teenager is ever to become a productive member of society, even the most limited relationship ability should be individually supported and encouraged. A useful treatment program should have the flexibility and the therapeutic strength to support even the most minimal and the most disturbed individual capability for emotional growth and personal relationship interaction.

The whole residential unit program should be geared to encourage the adolescent's move into society at as high a level of social competence as he is capable. Implicit in this treatment approach is what Bettelheim and Sylvester (1948), call an "inner cohesiveness," the necessary integration of control, support, direction, and gratification for each individual teenager. With the support of the total treatment team and the peer-patient group, the disturbed adolescent learns first how to control, then how to channel, and finally how to use his energies in a growth-producing fashion. Formerly uncontrolled aggressiveness must first be contained, then channelled into an activity such as boxing with a punching bag, and finally directed into active competitive, growth-producing team sports. Socially intolerable sexual exhibitionism becomes acceptable to the community and emotionally gratifying to the teenager when this exhibitionism is channelled constructively into drama production (Curran, 1939). Disruptive, destructive anger may be structured productively into the hammering and the banging of the wood shop or into the noise and the energy of the jangling piano. With the control, the direction, and the personal example provided by the members of the caring team, these disturbed adolescents are weaned away from egocentric, autistic, nonproductive patterns of behavior toward socially acceptable, growth-producing forms of coping.

While the residential unit must constantly be directed toward accentuating and encouraging the individual capabilities of the adolescent patient, this treatment support must be realistically based on the intellectual, physical, and emotional capability of each teenager. A treatment program that sets goals which are not rationally attainable may so overburden the adolescent as to cause emotional disruption rather than growth. Attendance at a public school demands from the adolescent a high level of ego competence which he does not have at the time of hospital admission. If grossly disturbed teenagers are admitted to the inpatient setting and are then immediately encouraged and expected to attend a public school away from the environmental supports of the treatment unit, the teenage patient is placed in a totally impossible, potentially disorganizing situation. He is admitted to the residential unit so that he may receive external strengthening and direction; yet he is expected to carry the social and educational responsibility of attendance at a school outside the protective hospital setting. Such a poorly considered, badly integrated treatment program may lead only to disruptive anxiety in the disturbed adolescent and to further emotional regression. For the more disturbed teenager, the growth opportunity provided through academic achievement must be available within the supportive hospital environment. An inpatient school program must be totally integrated with the total treatment approach so that the school environment can enhance and support the individual growth of the teenager, as far as the teenager is capable of growing at that moment. Specific school subjects can be prescribed according to

27

the needs of the individual adolescent to enhance specific growth potentials. While the psychotic adolescent might find the abstract concepts of geometry or poetry disturbing and disruptive, the repetitive learning of historical or geographical facts might help enhance the development of necessary compulsive defenses. The emotional freedom of a sculpture class might arouse too many primitive feelings in the disturbed, emotionally unstructured adolescent, whereas a paint-by-number art task might help him begin to express feelings colorfully, yet in an organized fashion. While the uncertain adolescent patient might find it extremely difficult to relate closely to parenting female figures, he may be able to tolerate a structured relationship with a woman teacher in a planned classroom setting.

To promote individual adolescent growth, to enhance existing capabilities and to encourage relationship development, an adolescent treatment unit requires a wide range of graduated, growth-promoting treatment facilities which should be integrated in a total therapeutic program.

THE RESIDENTIAL STAFF

The final therapeutic effect of a residential treatment unit is totally dependent on the quality and the effectiveness of the treatment personnel. Every person who comes in contact with the adolescent patient must be considered an important member of the therapeutic team. For some disturbed teenagers, as they move toward emotional health, contacts with the kitchen maid, the maintenance man, or the gardener may be therapeutically much more important and beneficial than their prescribed, individual psychotherapy appointments. Each treatment interaction and relationship should integrate with and be integrated with each other interaction. Bettelheim (1966) emphasizes that, for him, the thorniest problem in a residential treatment center is the training of staff. Perhaps an even more difficult task is the initial selection of these staff members for a residential treatment group. Since these treatment personnel provide the consistent external ego supports and the personal direction needed by the disturbed teenager, the personal emotional integrity and strength of each individual staff member is of crucial treatment importance (Marcuse, 1967). As the adolescent patient begins to learn to relate comfortably and to handle his inner anxieties constructively, he will use the members of the treatment staff as his nearest identification examples, as models he uses positively and negatively. The members of this therapeutic team must be able to live constructively with their own emotional potentials and their own personal limitations. Too many parenting figures have already told these disturbed adolescents, "Do what I say but do not do what I do." By their day-to-day living example, the treatment team members show the adolescent patient what he can do and why such behavior is preferable.

There is no infallible rule for selecting good staff personnel to deal with adolescents. The treatment team should look for fellow human beings with normal strengths and capabilities, people who are able to live productively with themselves. Staff members should not attempt to be perfect but should try to do their best. If a member of the therapeutic staff is secure in his own self-worth but yet aware of his limitations and sensitivities, he can use these individual capabilities to help the disturbed teenagers toward greater emotional growth. The individual team member has to accept the reality that, with his personal strengths and his specific limitations, he will be able to help some adolescent patients but yet will have little overt effect on others. If staff personnel have the emotional need to save and to be successful, they will fail in their treatment goal. Since the task of the caring staff is to enhance and strengthen the individuality of these adolescents, the rewards for the treatment team must come when these teenagers succeed in their own individuality and in their own personal capabilities. If a treatment team member is alert to his own special sensitivities, he can be more diagnostically and therapeutically attuned to the nuances of his teenage patients. Staff members must have suffi-

29

cient personal security so that they can use their own inner feelings as ongoing diagnostic cues and treatment indicators in their interaction with their adolescent patients. If treatment personnel need to deny their personal reactions, they may blind themselves to the emotional status of individual patients and of the residential group (Hirschberg and Mandelbaum, 1957; Rosen, 1963; Caplan, 1966). If a staff member knows that, when he becomes angry, he tends to withdraw, his realization that he is withdrawing from a teenage patient should signal to him that there is something about this patient that is making him angry—a very valid diagnostic and treatment cue. He should then be able to consider his relationship with this teenager, on his own or with consultation, so that he can gain a better understanding of the teenager and thereby help the patient more effectively. Most teenage patients are extremely sensitive to staff idiosyncrasies, and use these behavior patterns to keep the treatment team at a distance. When a teenage patient learns that a young nurse withdraws emotionally when she is confronted with any erotized situation, he may deliberately act seductively to keep the nurse away from him—to isolate himself from her intrusion. If the nurse is aware that she responds in this fashion, she can use her personal feelings as a valid diagnostic indicator about the reaction this teenager provokes. At an appropriate time, the nurse might wish to discuss with the adolescent why he needs to react to her in this fashion and to consider with him whether they can interact together more productively. Treatment team members who are aware of the personal strengths and the individual sensitivities of each other can evaluate the relationship of other team members with individual patients and, as team members, can use this diagnostic understanding in an integrated therapeutic program (Warme, 1965; Christ and Wagner, 1966).

The members of the treatment team must be available to the adolescent patient not only for control but also as permanent identification models. These opportunities for identification must be based on the adolescent's realistic capabilities and potentials. If the disturbed teenager has a functioning intelligence quotient of 80, it is untherapeutic and unrealistic to surround him exclusively with college students and university trained psychiatrists and psychologists who encourage only intellectual growth and sublimation. Such an intellectually limited teenager would find it difficult and perhaps impossible to identify with such treatment team members. A continued day-to-day interaction with a gardener or a cook would provide this patient with a much more appropriate identification model. The intellectually limited adolescent could learn gratification from manual work and from close physical relationships. The young teenager with an intelligence level in the superior range must have available to him treatment personnel who can use words of more than one syllable; he requires the emotional gratification and growth opportunities of intellectual competition and mastery. If he is surrounded only by staff personnel whose sole interest is the latest football score or the fluctuating supermarket prices, intellectually and emotionally he will be frustrated and his growth energy wasted. The treatment team should thus be composed of individuals who are comfortable working together yet have their own discrete individuality and patterns of personal gratification.

While every person with whom the adolescent patient interacts must be considered a vital member of the treatment team, the total therapeutic program must be integrated and must be given direction by a focal authority. The adolescent patient and the caring staff need the security and the certainty of a final decision-making person, a definite, obvious team leader. This leader of the treatment team, be he a senior child-care worker, a psychologist, a social worker, or a psychiatrist, must be someone with whom the patients and the team members can relate meaningfully and for whom they can have sincere respect. Such a treatment team leader must be able to interact directly and intuitively with his individual staff members and with his adolescent patients. The role of the team leader is to integrate, coordinate, and direct. While the leader makes the final decision and gives the final integration to the team process, his clinical functioning and effectiveness is dependent on his sensitivity not only to the needs and the capabilities of his adolescent patients but also to the strengths and the limitations of his treatment staff.

In the final adolescent identification process, the teenage patient must identify meaningfully with an adult of the same sex. For adolescent boys, optimally, the treatment team leader should be a comfortable secure male; for adolescent girls the treatment team leader should be a warm feminine woman. If this leader of the therapeutic team, the major identification model for the adolescent patient in the residential unit, is of the opposite sex, most adolescent patients would experience disturbing and distressing feelings from which they might have to flee in such an identification process. The adolescent girl is liable to have frankly sexualized feelings toward a male team leader. These emotions, many of them natural and normal, can be so anxiety provoking that she might resort to sexual and self-destructive acting out. The teenage boy would find a relationship with a female team leader either unbearably dependent or excessively erotized; he might have to prove his masculinity and his independence too much by unproductive behavior. In the intense treatment relationships that evolve in an adolescent unit, the leader of the caring team sets the final pattern and gives the most significant identification model. With the intense interaction that develops between treatment team members and the adolescent patients, a therapeutically effective treatment unit quickly becomes patterned in the mold of the treatment team leader. In the final essay, this unit cohesiveness yields the greatest therapeutic strength and growth potential.

The treatment efficiency and purpose of any inpatient facility depends on the unit opportunities for control and growth stimulation, on the integrity, sensitivity, and integration of staff members and on the ability of the treatment team leader to coordinate the various resources available to him for the formulation of a meaningful program. When residential treatment is recommended for a disturbed adolescent, this specific prescription should be made with an understanding of the teenager's specific needs and of the treatment facility most suitable to meet his requirements.

Chapter III

The Continued Diagnostic Process in Residential Treatment

From the moment of his admission until the time he leaves the hospital setting, the adolescent patient should be the focus of an ongoing diagnostic evaluation. The emotional defenses of the disturbed teenager are so fluctuant and his coping ability is so variable that it is essential to know his immediate personality status in order that the treatment team may deal with him beneficially and can respond to him therapeutically at that specific moment. Because the disturbed adolescent has both a high energy potential for rapid growth and a tendency to regress markedly under stress, it is necessary to know in what direction he is moving emotionally at each particular instance. If the adolescent has been able to change from an infantile emotional position to a more mature level of functioning, it would be folly if the treatment personnel continue to deal with him as with an infant. If, under stress, the teenager has abandoned a mature pattern of behavior for a more regressed, narcissistic attitude, it is vital that the staff adjust with him in their relationship expectations. Many of the treatment mishaps in a therapeutic setting come where the treatment team do not appreciate that the young patient has made a significant emotional shift.

Even the normal adolescent hesitates and finds it difficult to share openly his feelings, his hopes and his goals. Because the emotionally sick adolescent has been hurt and repeatedly disappointed, he is more uncertain, more distrustful and even more cautious than the usual teenager about sharing his feelings directly. In many psychiatric treatment centers, the caring staff are conditioned to respond only to verbal communications from their patients. With the disturbed adolescent these verbal communications either will not be forthcoming or will be given only when the patient is well along the road to health. To gain the maximum understanding of the teenager's emotional status and to appreciate how best they can help him in the treatment setting, it is necessary for all members of the treatment staff to utilize every diagnostic cue made available in the adolescent patient's total daily living. In whatever the teenage patient does and with whatever he reacts, the treatment team must measure how this reflects on that patient's emotional integration, his individuality, and the quality of his relationship capability. By reading the adolescent's self-expression in his everyday environment, in his dress and physical appearance, and in his ongoing relationships, a constantly valid diagnostic evaluation can be made of every teenage patient. Since this diagnostic information is given by the young patient at a preverbal, unconscious level, the adolescent is usually not directly aware of how much he has shared of his self. Since the teenager is not fully conscious of these communications, open and direct staff interpretation of such diagnostic material would make the patient feel as if he had been "stripped" and his very integrity violated. These nonverbal communications made available by the adolescent in his environment, his appearance, and his behavior must be accepted quietly, sensitively, and intuitively by the treatment personnel but nonetheless most actively integrated in the total diagnostic and treatment process.

The Individual Diagnostic Process

Some treatment institutions, in the interest of conformity, security, and cleanliness, insist on complete uniformity with respect to the patient's living quarters, dress, and activities. Other treatment centers because of lack of funds demand that each patient conform totally to a hospital pattern. In reality, such a blanketing treatment approach tends to destroy the nascent individuality of the patient and to perpetuate or bring about an institutional or autistic pattern of behavior (Barton, 1966). Such enforced regimentation and institutionalization is probably the most costly form of treatment, both in terms of the long-term expenditure of funds needed for each patient and also when the waste and the destruction of human resources and capabilities in such an environment are considered. Where individual patients are forced into institutional patterns, the treatment staff lose diagnostic information that would allow them to be more efficient and more accurate in whatever treatment program they attempt. If the caring staff are ever to return these patients to society, they must augment whatever individual strengths the disturbed patient has and they must reinforce whatever self-confidence he possesses. Hopefully even in the most untherapeutic, inefficient, institutionalized treatment situation, most patients can fight total regimentation and can insist that some aspects of their life continue personal, individual, and private. In a meaningfully therapeutic setting, patients need to be given the opportunity and the encouragement to be individuals and to express their individuality. Such personal self-expression not only gives the treatment team a more accurate appraisal of the patient's emotional status but also allows the patient himself to face the realistic meaning of his individuality (Easson, 1967a). In the optimum treatment environment where the patient is allowed reasonable self-expression, he then has to face what kind of self he is expressing and how this measures up against the reality of society's needs and of his own expectations. Diagnostically, this clinical information and these communications given by the patient at a nonverbal level can be considered from three aspects:

1. The Level of Organization

If the teenage patient is confused in his thinking, he cannot establish for himself an organized environment. His self-expression, as shown in his surroundings, his appearance, and his interactions, can only reflect his inner disorganization. If his thinking and feeling processes are under reasonable control and direction, his nonverbal forms of self-expression will be similarly organized and integrated. The level of the adolescent patient's emotional organization is accurately reflected by the organization shown in his living environment, his mode of dressing, and his pattern of relating.

2. The Quality of Self-Expression

Where the adolescent patient is impoverished in thought and in emotion, his forms of self-expression will be similarly bland, sparse, and lacking in depth. Where he has a deep emotional life, his pattern of interaction and his fashions of self-expression will be similarly rich and expressive. Where he feels strongly in a specific direction, his surroundings will echo such definite feelings. The richness of a teenager's feelings is reflected by the rich self-expression he shows. Conflictual emotions are shown by contradictory forms of behavior, dress, or environmental decoration.

3. The Individual Specificity of Self-Expression

The teenager's environment, appearance, and social activities will reflect his personal interests, impulses, and struggles. The emotions occupying his thoughts and feelings at a specific time will be most clearly reflected in the individual and social significance of the self-expression he shows in his room, in his style of clothes, and in the friends with whom he congregates. Most adolescents at every level of emotional competence will not share in an open verbal fashion this kind of personal information. The treatment team need not wait to be told verbally by the teenage patient how he is feeling and what he is feeling; from his nonverbal communication they can readily read all they need to know.

In our day-to-day living with teenagers and with people of all ages, we constantly use these nonverbal cues. In the continuous treatment of the disturbed adolescent, it is most important to be more consciously aware of this diagnostic information and to integrate this understanding into the total treatment process.

SELF-EXPRESSION IN THE ENVIRONMENT

Treatment-supported individual self-expression is of crucial importance in the continued diagnostic evaluation of the adolescent patient. In the hospital setting, optimally the teenager has some area that he can confidently feel is his own. This is a place where somehow he can be himself and express himself accordingly. At best, this private area should be a room of his own but, through hospital necessity, it may only be an area around his bed, his locker, or his shelf; his private area may be away from his sleeping and living quarters and can well be a small garden plot hidden away on the grounds, a school locker or a private shoe box stacked in a communal closet. In this individual place where the adolescent patient feels free to be himself, the treatment staff by merely looking and observing can gain a very meaningful diagnostic impression of the state of the patient's total personality. All possessions of an adolescent are very meaningful extensions of his personality (Redl and Wineman, 1957, p. 96); since these personal belongings are such significant self-extensions and self-communications, they must be respected and valued by all the treatment staff. The writer would disagree most strongly with the Layfayette Clinic group (Beckett, 1965, p. 131) where they suggest that routine, irregular searches of patients' rooms should be undertaken as part of hospital policy; such searches are an unwarranted, disrespectful invasion of teenage privacy and tend to depreciate and to limit necessary, therapeutic individual self-expression and emotional growth. If searches are essential from the point of view of hospital security, of the group treatment, or of the individual patient, these searches should be carried out only with the teenager present so that he learns that both he and his possessions are respected and will not be invaded without his knowledge and preferably only with his coopera-tion. For the more disturbed adolescents, the fragile psychotic teenager or the immature, childlike young man or young woman, a search of their possessions may be such an intrusion of their personal integrity that an emotional disruption may be precipitated: for these very disturbed teenagers, any such searching intrusion is totally and absolutely contraindicated.

The teenage patient's room tends to reflect his level of basic emotional integration. The confused patient will not have an organized living environment. He does not have the ability to organize his room. His living quarters will be a mess and a clutter. The cleaning staff will complain that his room is in constant disarray. The treatment personnel will find that al-though they can help him to arrange his room temporarily through outside support (just as they can give some semblance of organization to his thinking and behavior), merely hours later his room is again disorganized as the patient is basically disorganized. To the compulsive, rigid patient, a messy environ-ronment is a personal anathema. His room is likely to be cold and cheerless with his belongings neatly piled and stored. Magazines and newspapers for weeks and years past will be stacked methodically. His bed will be carefully arranged and his clothes geometrically placed in their appropriate drawers. The quality of the room organization can give many valid cues as to whether the obsessive patient is defending against an inner psychotic confusion or whether he has the more stable personality integration of the compulsive neurotic. Where the adolescent is organizing his inner psychotic confusion by the use of rigid compulsive defenses, the belongings in his living environment are typically arranged without real emotional ap-preciation of the different social values and personal uses. A prized, fragile phonograph may be laden down with ancient magazines and dirty clothes. Treasured letters or mementos may be stored away with school essays, discarded sandwiches, and record club announcements. The patient's environment re-flects his basic inability to differentiate at this level of psychosis between the emotional quality of different relationships and different possessions. On the other hand, the compulsive neurotic is much more sensitive to the nuances of human relationships and to the different significances of his belongings. While the things he owns may be stacked, they are piled with more appropriateness and more purpose; the compulsive neurotic shows a definite selectivity and an ability to plan for his future needs. He categorizes his possessions according to their emotional and social significance. Though both the obsessive psychotic and the obsessive neurotic may present with outwardly similar patterns of behavior, their basic emotional strengths and capabilities are very different. The treatment approach for the compulsive neurotic would prove disastrous for the obsessive psychotic. The treatment team must help the psychotic patient strengthen his compulsive defenses so that he can bring organization to his environment and his inner confusion. It may be months or years before the compulsive psychotic develops sufficient ego strength to give up some of his obsessive rigidity. The obsessive neurotic, however, can be encouraged by the treatment team to venture into situations less structured and less predictable. With the basic emotional integrity of the neurotic, the compulsive neurotic adolescent can often be encouraged early in the treatment process to relinquish his compulsive defenses in favor of more flexible patterns of behavior. The treatment personnel can gauge this vitally important diagnostic difference between the obsessive psychotic and the obsessive neurotic by merely observing the teenage patient's living area. Under stress, as the obsessive psychotic patient begins to find that his compulsive defenses are inadequate to handle his inner confusion, his room may begin to show more confusion and disorganization. On the other hand, when the psychotic teenager is beginning to develop more emotional strength and flexibility, he will first show increased personal sensitivity and foresight in the organization and the self-expression demonstrated in his environment. He may still arrange his possessions in piles but the piles may now be more selective and appropriate. With the next week in mind he may start to anticipate in his room arrangement exactly what he will need tomorrow or the next day.

The room of the activity oriented adolescent may scream action from the walls—menacing, speeding cars, pugnacious boxers, blatant advertisements exhorting to smoke, to drink or to rebel. Grotesque masks, misshapen figures, and monstrous caricatures may mock mother, father, family, hospital and country. As the teenager prepares to elope, maps may appear in his room and the name tabs disappear from his clothes; these are often very ostentatious, direct communications which are open and available to staff members who are willing to see and to understand. Frequently as the teenager prepares to leave his environment, he removes his more personal and more favored self-expressions—his prized photographs and mementos disappear from his living area—thereby indicating nonverbally his plan to relocate. The room of the adolescent boy reflects his comfort in his sexual identity by virtue of the masculine athletic equipment strewn around and by the adventure and the hotrod magazines or comics displayed. For those young men less certain in their masculinity, there may be easily seen magazines with pictures of overly muscular young men and boxing journals with advertisements offering courses for "boys" who want to become "men." Where the uncertain, inadequate teenager has to deny too strongly the marked regressive pull to remain dependent on his family and on his culture, his room may blaringly proclaim his extreme defiance of parental or cultural ideas. The Jewish boy may festoon his living quarters with pictures of the former Nazi Führer or with menacing swastikas. The teenage girl from the prim and proper white Anglo-Saxon Protestant community may cover her wall with photographs from her favorite Negro culture magazines. While the adolescent girl may have a room that is outwardly warmly feminine, the casually appearing male pinup magazines may suggest that she still struggles with her own feminine identification. While she emphasizes that her latest romance is based

41

on the deepest and most meaningful love, the fashion whereby she has added yet another picture to her collection of boyfriends on display may demonstrate very clearly how this young lady, for her own personal security, needs the comfort of a large collection of admirers. This diagnostic impression may be further strengthened by her tendency to pin on her bulletin board the most private communications from her latest beloved in which he tells her how wonderful and meaningful she really is to him. The nightmarish fantasies of the teenager are often readily indicated by the collection of bizarre and frequently blatantly crude horror magazines and paperbacks. In the room of the young man or young woman whose sexual feelings are still too much fused with aggressive drives, sadistic Nazi or Japanese muscle men may be observed on openly displayed reading material, torturing bosomy maidens. More covert sexual conflict may be indicated by the copy of "Vogue" hidden away in the young man's desk drawer or by the silk underwear he has surreptitiously bought for himself.

The quality of the adolescent's relationship ability is reflected in his surroundings. The narcissism of the teenager may be shown by his expensive collection of perfumes and potions with which he needs to preen himself, or by his vast accumulation of clothes. The walls of his room may be plastered with photographs of adored friends but, on a closer inspection, the most prominent person in the pictures may be the teenager himself. The rooms of some adolescents may be totally devoid of human photographs where the adolescent has only minimal relationship capability or where he cannot admit to himself his need for trusting relationships. Where the more disturbed adolescent finds it difficult to maintain a meaningful relationship in his own thinking and emotional integration, he may display around his room part objects of the meaningful person—belongings from the loved one to emphasize in a necessary concrete fashion to the teenager that the relationship does continue, and that the loved person is still available somewhere though not immediately present in the flesh. In surprisingly

42

open fashion, adolescents may demonstrate how strongly they feel the urge to regress. Jokingly, the teenager may maintain for months or years on his bulletin board a baby rattle given to him. Not uncommonly, a worldly wise young man or young woman may have a stuffed doll or a teddy bear—for decoration only, of course—but often this stuffed toy seems to find its way into bed with the owner. The autistic teenager, living in his own inner world, exists in an environment devoid of warmth, ornamentation, or overt relating. The walls of his room may be bleak and bare. As he begins to relate to people, this incipient relationship ability may be reflected in the very small decorations that begin to appear in his environment. Frequently the psychotic or the severely disturbed teenager shows his beginning relationship ability by decorating his room with an occasional small picture of a horse or an animal. At this very uncertain stage of relationships, it is often much more comfortable for this severely disturbed patient to relate first to some animal rather than to a human being, to something that is alive but still not identifiable as a person. Frequently, as their relationship ability grows, these severely disturbed adolescents will begin to relate next in their environment to pictures of idealized human beings, to the late President Kennedy, to Abraham Lincoln, to a distant popular music singer or to a sanctified religious figure. Much later in their self-expression, these patients may begin to admit that they do care for fallible individual human beings by displaying photographs of peer friends and then of family members.

Through every expressive and perceptual modality the adolescent expresses himself in his environment. When the nurse comments that an adolescent boy's room smells like "a ladies' beauty parlor," she is highlighting a valid diagnostic cue—she has clarified that the smell in this muscular young man's room is that of feminine perfume. In this nonverbal way, this young man was pointing up some of his struggles over his own masculine identity; because of his emotional conflicts he was concealing the masculine smells of sweat and semen by the use of these

43

perfumes. When the teenager's room smells of glue, it does not necessarily indicate that he has developed a sudden, avid interest in handicrafts but more likely, it suggests that he is sniffing himself into a glue-induced intoxication as one way of handling his tensions. A room most thoroughly sprinkled with deodorizer might cause the staff to wonder what underlying scent was being hidden, denied or deodorized away; could it be the smell of contraband alcohol, tobacco, or marijuana. A pervasive odor of shoe polish might suggest a compulsive need for shoe cleaning but also may point out the adolescent who had discovered that by heating and smelling the fumes from shoe polish he could develop at least a fancied "high."

Most often the treatment team members need look no further than the displays in the adolescent's room to know with what specific problems the teenager is struggling. Where smoking or drinking is forbidden and somehow the adolescent finds himself able to decorate his room with empty cigarette packs or beer cans, it is usually a most direct communication to the staff that the adolescent is successfully flouting authority. It is equally interesting how often the treatment staff manages not to see such a message and by such circumscribed blindness continues to support and encourage the adolescent in acting out his anxieties. The teenage patients quickly discover that the best way to "hide" contraband is to hang it openly on display. On the adolescent wall may be suspended a gallon jar of root-beer which is successfully being brewed into a more potent alcoholic mixture, right under the staff's eyes and noses. Where there is any question about sexual acting out between patients, usually the patients' rooms give very valid cues. If the teenager's room is papered with seductive photographs of the loved one, it would be futile for the staff to deny that the two adolescents are in some way considering a mutual seduction. Diagnostically, the staff members need to seek no further than to observe what is displayed before their eyes—if they are willing to see and to comprehend.

For most teenagers, there is usually some main place of special self-expression. If the adolescent patient has his own room, frequently this focal point is a bulletin board or a dresser top in front of a mirror. Within this comparatively small area, the adolescent's total personality may be brought into relief. On a bulletin board, the teenager may display very valid and readily usable, diagnostic material in the form of announcements of dates and future goals, letters and ticket stubs from past activities and past relationships, and photographs picturing the meaningful relationships in his life. In such a small nuclear area, the teenager may bring into focus his level of emotional organization, his relationship capability, the quality and depth of his feelings and his specific areas of marked personal interest and conflict.

SELF-EXPRESSION IN PHYSICAL APPEARANCE AND IN CLOTHES

The teenager expresses himself very directly in the clothes he wears. The adolescent patient's emotional organization is reflected in the organization of his clothing. If the young lady comes to the dining room with her hair awry, her dress buttoned askew, without stockings, and with scuffed shoes, the treatment staff can reasonably assume that she is in a state of emotional disarray. If the young man sits around the residential unit dressed in a bland white t-shirt, scuffy colorless beige pants, and nondescript, uncleaned shoes, the child care workers would be realistic in assuming that his washed-out appearance and outwardly apathetic behavior give an accurate reflection of his inner emotional status. When the teenager bounces into school dressed in shorts and a kindergarten sweat shirt, the teaching staff has already been told by his regressed appearance that emotionally he is not at that moment at a level of adolescent competence. Certain modes of dressing have both individual and group significance. The young lady who goes to public school in a shirt emblazoned "69," with its heterosexual and homosexual connotations, trumpets somewhat too loudly her need to defy sexual convention. The young man who parades around the unit wearing a t-shirt ornamented with grotesque "weirdos" is proclaiming openly his grotesque self-concept. The teenage boy wearing an earring or ankle bracelet is openly sharing his confused sexual conflicts. Cutoff jeans may be comfortable and suitable for private relaxation but when they are cut off at the groin level and worn on every social occasion, they suggest that the adolescent wearer has perhaps too much need to exhibit. Form fitting and hip hugging clothes may be indeed fashionable but often these clothes and the patients who wear them leave much too little to the imagination. The teenage patient can be asked why he has the need to reveal so much and what he is specifically trying to demonstrate. As with other nonverbal communications, frequently nonverbal interpretations can be offered to the patient with therapeutic results. An outbreak of very tight pants among the young males in an adolescent unit came to an abrupt halt when, one evening as the boys waited in the cafeteria line, the hospital doctor appeared with a ruler and notebook and from a distance ostentatiously measured and noted down the obvious size of each young man's genitals—no other interpretation was necessary. By the next morning somehow these young gentlemen had started to wear pants several sizes larger.

As all parents know, teenagers tend to dress in keeping with specific emotional struggles. If a disturbed adolescent feels he is liable to explode in disruptive behavior, he may change his favorite clothing to more tattered, less valued clothes. In a treatment unit, the residential staff always knew when a 15 year old girl patient was planning to elope as invariably she wore in preparation for such departures a pair of shoddy, torn sneakers—her "runaway shoes" as the staff learned to call them. In the early fall, treatment team members on another residential unit noted a young patient parading around the ward in his heavy winter coat; in some way this adolescent boy wanted the staff to know that he was contemplating a runaway, for why else would he need such heavy protection against the nighttime cold. When this very obvious nonverbal message was ignored by the staff, the teenager told a member of the treatment team very directly that he was contemplating an elopement. When still no action was taken and no support was given, the boy had then no option but to run. Runaways commonly occur when nonverbal and even verbal messages are studiously ignored by treatment staff so that eventually the patient has no solution but to elope. If he does not run away, he may lose too much "face" with his peers and in his own eyes.

For the younger adolescent, strict conformity to group styles of dressing is age appropriate. The boys in grades eight and nine of junior high school normally and naturally tend to dress alike and to have similar hair styles. With the older teenager and the young adult, there is more self-confidence and individuality which should be reflected in his dress and appearance. When a 17, 18 or 19 year old young man or young woman is steadfastly clinging to a group-dictated fashion of dressing such a dress style would suggest that this particular adolescent does not yet have the personal security to allow him to make and to maintain an individual choice; rather such an adolescent still requires the ego support and the ego identity provided by the peer group styles. Diagnostically it is essential for any treatment team member working with teenage patients to know the normal and the accepted patterns in the local teenage group culture.

For the young lady, masculine jeans and flapping male shirts may be relaxing for the activities of the moment but when such male clothing is maintained as a constant pattern of dress, this style does suggest to the observing treatment team that the adolescent girl is uncomfortable and insecure in her feminine role and identity. For the teenage girl, a pink dress might be appropriately feminine but were her male escort to dress too often in his pretty pink shirt and lovely pink socks, his masculine security and sexual identity might be questioned with reason. For such a young man, sturdy blues, blacks, browns and reds are somewhat more appropriate to normal masculine drive and aggression, though the constant flashiness of scarlet shirts and vermillion socks might point to a young man who did not yet have full control over his aggressive impulses. Black and somber clothes may be an excellent indication of sadness and of mourning; the drab and disconsolate adolescent tends to wear drab and disconsolate colors. This personal color preference should not, of course, be confused with the cultural preference which presently favors black as a delinquent color. Black tight pants, black t-shirt, black high-heeled leather boots, and black leather jackets are all worn by young men and women who aspire to be members of "Hell's Angels," and in this way attempt to borrow an identity for themselves.

The emotional struggles of the adolescent are closely mirrored in his physical appearance and carriage. The rigidly controlled teenager walks stiffly; his arms do not swing freely and his body is carried as one piece. This bodily rigidity reflects his emotional inflexibility and the inner reality that he barely controls his impulses and confusions. Muscular tiredness, the back that is bowed, and the face that is drawn and haggard may mirror deep inner depression in a suffering teenager. As the adolescent tries to change his identity and his self-concept, he may reflect his emotional shifts and uncertainties in his hair style and color—the blond California surf bum, the black-haired Romeo, the mousey brown Milquetoast. The teenage girl may silver her hair in attempted middle-aged sophistication, darken her waves as a ravishing brunette, or bleach her locks as the blonde bombshell. In both teenage boys and girls the hair may be styled in defiant disarray, coquettishly curled, or childishly slicked forward. The boy's sideburns may rise and fall depending on his emotional need to proclaim loudly his ability to grow hair and to defy certain cultural expectations. The inner fluctuations of sexual tensions may be reflected in the outward variation of facial and body acne. Child-care workers may gauge whether a boy is finding expression for his sexual drives by the condition of his skin; with some adolescents, acne seems to lessen when they begin to act out sexual feelings or to use these impulses in socially acceptable sublimations. Inner tensions and angers may be outwardly reflected by facial picking and rubbing. Where a teenager's physical appearance is bizarre, his inner emotional integration is liable to be tenuous. Where the adolescent plucks out his eye lashes, in some way he is trying to erase a significant part of his self-identity. When a teenager plucks out his eyebrows, which normally are zealously protected, it is likely that such an adolescent is psychotic; many of these more disturbed adolescents chew and swallow their hair with extremely primitive and bizarre fantasies.

The Group Diagnostic Process

The experienced treatment staff member should be able to make an accurate estimation of the emotional status of individual adolescents and of the adolescent group as a whole, merely by walking through the dining room at mealtimes (Polsky, 1962; Rubenfeld and Stafford, 1963; Almond and Esser, 1965). The sensitive worker can gauge from the amount the teenager eats and frequently from the type of food he eats the quality and the level of the adolescent's anxiety. The teenager's style of eating may give clues as to his emotional status. Where the adolescent has a constant diet of peanut butter and jelly sandwiches, food which is more appropriate to the grade school child, it may be an indication that emotionally he is functioning at a preadolescent level. Many disturbed adolescents actually do not know how to eat in a socially acceptable fashion because during the normal age period for social training they were caught up in emotional environmental turmoil. Where the psychotic teenager has no concept of long-term goals and lacks the ability to delay even the simplest gratification, his eating may be merely a shovelling-in of food to assuage his hunger tension. The obese adolescent who overeats both to soothe his anxieties and to gain attention by his gluttony, ostentatiously waddles back to the kitchen for second or third helpings of food; the angry social rejection provoked by this exhibitionistic behavior makes him even more anxious and more liable to overeat. The anorexic teenager so obviously refuses food that she gains both attention and rejection. Insofar as her inner tensions are accentuated by the environmental reaction, she is prompted further to refuse food. Miller (1964, p. 180) relates how the milk intake rose markedly when his group of adolescent boys became anxious. Specific foods may be favored or fashionable with the adolescent group when these foods are rumored to increase virility or sexual attractiveness. The monthly weighing of healthy teenagers is useful in demonstrating how their weight levels fluctuate directly with their tensions; these weight variations must of course be differentiated from the gains of normal teenage growth.

In a treatment setting, the therapeutic personnel will be able to notice which adolescents congregate together and how they interact one with another (Kellam, Shmelzer, and Berman, 1966). The delinquent "rebellious" group will tend to sit together. The passive, quiescent teenagers and the disorganized adolescents will often sit in one group and attract to this less demanding social nucleus staff members who wish a temporary haven of peace. A few individualists in the treatment unit may select for the day other individuals with whom they wish to sit or they may decide to sit apart by themselves. The paranoid, insecure patients locate themselves at specific vantage points so that they can eye everyone and everything watchfully. Each patient group has its leader, its followers, and usually its challenger to the leader. These social reactions within each patient group are reflected by the group sitting arrangements and the attitudes of group members around the dining room table and in the unit living room. The rebels hunch together talking in whispers, making as if they have some deep, dark secret—whereas in reality their main secret is their basic profound inadequacy and personal insecurity—a secret to none but themselves. The disorganized adolescent in the treatment unit will tend to ally himself with a source of external emotional strength and direction, an adolescent patient leader or a staff member—perhaps not in direct conversation but frequently by merely sitting alongside or nearby that person. The treatment team member can gauge the tenor of an adolescent group by the group reaction to his presence in their midst. The dependent, clinging, overly uncertain teenager draws him into the group to provide group strength. The caring staff can feel almost a kind of emotional suction when in the proximity of such patients. The seductive, smothering teenage girl envelops the staff member with her attention and her conversation. The paranoid teenagers both invite caring personnel suspiciously and push them away invitingly. The rebellious teenage group so actively and so invariably try to exclude staff attention that they insure the maximum continued attention.

Within these adolescent patient peer groupings, the individual stability and the emotional security of group members can be readily ascertained through the nonverbal cues. The support of his group may be emotionally essential to the adolescent who is struggling toward independence yet still uncertain of his own integrity. Such a teenager may dress in every detail according to the group pattern and may fight tenaciously any outside attempt to change him from this group fashion. At this stage in his personality development, the group identity may be essential for his emotional functioning. Such a mutually supportive teenage grouping may be very obvious because the boys and girls of this group are all dressed exactly the same; they may have a group language and group signs. If such a group has a delinquent personality, the individual members are delinquent; if the group outwardly has a more mature, growth directed identity, the individual members will overtly appear individually more mature. The personality of a group is rarely static. The treatment personnel must be aware of significant movements within patient groups and across groups. As the disturbed teenager becomes emotionally stronger he may move to a leadership position within his specific group; at the time he attains leadership or even before he reaches such leadership, he may find his group too limiting and too regressive for his increased self-confidence and capabilities. Within the hospital setting where staff and patient expectations tend to maintain him in one pattern, his struggle to shed the group identity will tend to be resisted not only by his patient peer group but frequently also by the therapeutic personnel. His necessary separation from this group and his emotional growth to establish his own individual identity will require a great deal of staff understanding and support, both overtly and covertly.

Within the adolescent treatment unit, the teenage patients assume various roles which are supported consciously and unconsciously by members of the caring team (Polsky, 1962). Where a teenage patient or a staff member has become the scapegoat for unit anxieties, several circumstances tend to be present. Usually this patient or this staff member has isolated himself from his own peer group by some form of behavior that is unacceptable to his peers. In such a situation there develops tacit general support for the use of this isolated person as the unit scapegoat. The child-care worker who is seen by his fellow staff members as being much too weak may find himself placed in the position by his colleagues where he has to be punitively strong and thus the focus of unit anger. The teenager who is disturbingly crazy may find that somehow the treatment staff does not see that he is being teased and harried by his fellow patients; indeed he may find himself the butt of staff "jokes." The cause of such scapegoating may not be at first apparent but invariably it is something that causes staff and patient anxiety. Where a teenage patient is being scapegoated, it is necessary immediately to focus on whatever there is about this particular person that makes people around him angry and anxious. Is it the fact that he is crazy and that his particular brand of craziness disturbs us? Is it the fact that he is of a minority racial or religious group and that somehow he and we feel that he does not quite integrate with the total team? Is it possible that he has been totally ungrateful and unresponsive to our efforts to relate to him so we are angry at his ingratitude? Has he developed a special relationship to which we, as team members or as fellow adolescents, are not privy? Has he become isolated through becoming the favorite of a particular staff member or of a particular patient so that perhaps he is now the recipient of feelings that should be really directed toward this staff member or this patient? It can be taken as an established fact that scapegoating does not occur on a treatment unit without the agreement, conscious or unconscious, of both staff and patients.

Within the hospital ward, certain patients will become leaders, benevolent leaders and malevolent leaders. These leadership roles usually occur with direct and indirect staff support. If the treatment unit is subtly being terrorized by a particular young man, the treatment question must be raised as to how this teenager achieved such a position. It may then become apparent that there is something about this adolescent patient—his threats of emotional explosion, his homosexual appeal, his primitive bizarreness—which cause the treatment personnel and his fellow patients to see him as too powerful, too anxiety-provoking and as someone from whom they should keep a more comfortable distance. At the same time, it is obvious that, even if it is a patient who is in control of the treatment unit, the fact that the unit is being controlled and directed does take a certain amount of work and responsibility off staff shoulders. Especially at times of continued stress and turmoil, it is very easy to abdicate to the patients the staff responsibility for the control, the teaching, and the direction of the most disturbing and most disturbed adolescents. Where there is no open patient leadership in a treatment unit, the staff members must ask themselves why there is so little leadership striving. Is every member on the unit so confused, disorganized, and passive that he is incapable of providing leadership at a patient level? Is it that no adolescent patient at that time has a definite goal or a specific purpose, or could it be that treatment staff members have so over-reacted to individual enterprise and personal self-expression that, momentarily at least, individuality has been totally suppressed. Constantly, within the residential unit the status of the individual teenage patients and of the patient groups has to be weighed and evaluated, and shifts in the peer relationships and in the relationships with staff members have to be examined for their cues as to the teenager's emotional status (Shader, Kellam, and Durell, 1967).

In all the teenage patient's social activities, his emotional capabilities can be evaluated. His day-to-day progress at the swimming pool can give excellent indicators of his emotional integrity and of his ability to relate. How does he handle himself when he is half naked in a social setting? In such a coeducational activity is he bumbling and forward or backward and shy? Is he seductively arrogant or is he blandly distant? Does he nonchalantly perform on the diving board or does he clown and make a fool of himself? Within the hospital school, another facet of the teenager's life is available to this ongoing diagnostic process. In the physical education class, can he tolerate the open aggression of competitive sports and the physical contact of team activities? In the dressing room, does he exhibit himself or does he peep? In the small hospital classroom, can he tolerate academic demands for self-control and for the delay of immediate gratification? He has the opportunity to respond in the hospital school setting in a fashion which he knows will bring approval from his parents and society; he can strive for such approval or he can rebel and fight. He may find learning a gratifying personal growth experience which, however, he may have to disrupt because he cannot tolerate such pleasure or because such growth will take him to an unbearable level of responsibility. He may need to destroy his learning process as, self-destructively, he destroys his parental hopes and expectations. In this ongoing diagnostic treatment process school teachers, maintenance men, cooks, gardeners, nurses, aides and every member of the professional staff need to share with each other and to integrate their mutual understanding of the adolescent patient.

THE DIAGNOSTIC PROCESS
AWAY FROM THE HOSPITAL SETTING

As the adolescent develops increasing emotional capability, he is gradually allowed to test his strengths in less structured social settings outside the immediate hospital environment. Since these growth opportunities must be available, a treatment institution should not be too isolated or distant from social opportunities. The treatment and diagnostic process continues wherever and whenever the teenage patient moves into the general community. Many a disturbed adolescent has been able to maintain a front of self-sufficiency for himself and for treatment staff members until he was required to take a bus downtown on his own; only then has he had to confess that he did not understand the mechanics of a bus trip and that he was scared being alone by himself in the city or the village. As these disturbed adolescents have grown physically, they have missed the opportunity for many social activities and many natural learning experiences. Their profound naïvete and their marked ignorance may be an astounding revelation even to those treatment staff members who deal with them from day-to-day. So often in an inpatient treatment setting, the staff members are not fully aware of the magnitude of continued support and direction which they do provide to each patient. In an adolescent hospital unit, the treatment personnel were astounded and unbelieving when a 14 year old delinquent, nonpsychotic adolescent girl told them very honestly and very directly that she did not know the meaning of the street traffic signal colors. In the hospital environment she had been able to maintain a very successful façade of total social competence. When she was given the opportunity to visit with friends away from the hospital, her delinquent behavior began to recur. In the face of this signal of mounting inner anxiety she confessed to herself and to the treatment staff that she was woefully ignorant in many basic areas of social functioning.

Many of these disturbed teenagers are totally unaware and completely insensitive to normal social expectations. Frequently they do not know and do not understand the conversations and the interests of their normal adolescent peers. Their disturbed behavior often increases as a front to cover over their deep social inadequacies. They cannot allow themselves to go

55

to a high school ball game because they neither understand the game process nor do they know how to react to the game. Rather than place themselves in this impossible situation they provoke some disruption on the hospital unit so that they can be held back from the activity in a fashion where they can blame the treatment team and salvage their own pride. Individual patients should have the opportunity for slowly increasing social experiences as they are capable of tolerating such activities. In this movement away from the hospital setting the treatment staff must maintain a constant ongoing diagnostic process. Both in the hospital and in the teenager's interactions in the community, many cues are available to the treatment team. What movie does the teenager select, what television program does he favor, and why does he have such a preference? For many disturbed adolescents the easiest social identification they can make is with the multitude of community delinquencies portrayed in various social "entertainments." The bizarre, sadistic, inner fantasies of many young patients are acted out in gory detail as they watch from their car at the drive-in movie. The treatment staff needs to be sensitive and aware diagnostically that in making such movie and television selections, the adolescent is still sharing his inner feelings and struggles.

Once the adolescent patient has shown himself intellectually and emotionally capable within the hospital school setting, it may be judged therapeutically appropriate, after discussion with the teenager, to let him try himself in a public school setting. Such a treatment move to greater individual responsibilities and personal rewards provides an excellent opportunity for sensitive diagnostic evaluation. Any normal teenager entering a new school setting would be reasonably anxious and for the sick adolescent the anxiety experience is heightened. With his very limited emotional strength, the inpatient moves into the community school as a foreigner into a new country. The treatment staff must note whether the young patient blandly has to deny his worries or whether he can reasonably face and discuss his realistic anxieties and prepare to meet these tensions. In the public school setting, does he have to be rigidly inflexible or can he allow himself a moderate amount of variation from day-to-day? What kind of peer attention can he gain in the public school setting—in his anxiety, does he revert to being the clown, the delinquent or the "sickie" from the local "funny farm?" The public school teachers may need help and support in treating the patient in public school in exactly the same fashion as other students; frequently the sympathetic teacher tends to give the adolescent patient too much support so that he does not have the reality based growth experience that he requires in this ordinary social school setting.

The continued emotional functioning of the adolescent patient must be evaluated and integrated across the days and the weeks both in the inpatient and the outpatient environment. It may well be that he can maintain himself as outwardly appropriate in a community school setting, only to return to the residential unit and there regress and exhibit grossly bizarre behavior. In such an instance, the teenage patient has directly indicated to the treatment team that his comparatively limited personality strength is sufficient only to maintain ego integration through the school hours. This is a vitally important diagnostic understanding, both as to what can be expected from the patient at that moment and as to the emotional strengthening he will need to allow him to adapt completely to life totally outside a hospital setting. Other adolescent patients may maintain generally appropriate behavior in the hospital treatment setting only to be grossly disruptive in a public school environment, in a situation where they feel themselves too much challenged by authority figures. Some disturbed adolescents may find it impossible to succeed in any socially appropriate setting lest, in succeeding, they find themselves outside a protected environment facing responsibilities they cannot tolerate or giving up infantile gratifications they cannot yet relinquish.

No teenage interaction is more certain to raise staff anxiety and anger than an overtly sexual relationship (McNeil and

Morse, 1964; Easson, 1967b). The staff in treatment centers react to such open sexual relationships by forbidding them, by ignoring the reality of such relationships, or by too actively supporting such interactions. In reality, a meaningful understanding of such very important behavior can give the maximum diagnostic information as to the teenager's emotional capability and potential. Because sexuality is such an active driving force during adolescence, such emotional energy must be actively measured and channeled toward health. The members of the treatment team must allow themselves directly and realistically to be aware of such sexual feelings in the teenage patients and to use these emotional drives for the maximum growth and benefit of the adolescent. It is therapeutically disastrous to deny or to suppress these strong drives insofar as the adolescent patient will be totally unprepared to use this most prominent part of his personality in a continued useful growth-producing fashion, upon his return to society. It is frequently suggested that treatment staff members are made especially anxious by the sexual interactions of patients because allegedly treatment personnel, like everyone else, have not become absolutely comfortable in the management of their own sexual identity and drives. Such statements can equally be made about all other drives since none of us is totally comfortable in handling our instinctual urges, be they aggressive, sexual, or loving. What is most difficult for treatment team members to face is the reality that a sexual relationship between two teenagers may exclude the therapeutic staff; the treatment team are outsiders to this meaningful relationship and will become even more excluded if the relationship becomes more meaningful. While the long-term treatment goals are geared to help and support the adolescent to emancipate and to develop the capacity for forming deep personal relationships, it is most frequently around a sexually based relationship that the caring staff members struggle as to whether they can really allow the teenager to become independent of the treatment team. The treatment staff must face their own ambivalence about the adolescent patient's ability to separate from direct staff supervision, participation, and control.

In such a situation, it is essential that treatment team members clarify to themselves at what level of emotional maturity the teenager is functioning in this sexual relationship. For many more mature, more sensitive adolescents, the experience of "being in love" is the final decisive step toward meaningful emotional maturation. Where these disturbed adolescents have had difficulty in trusting and being trusted, their first love relationship may be their initial sustained experience of trust. With other less emotionally integrated teenagers, a sexualized relationship can be merely an avenue for instinctual gratification or for the acting out of inner anxieties and unreasonable angers. The treatment team must evaluate whether the adolescent patient is relating to his loved partner as merely to a gratifying part object, a preambivalently cathected Madonna or Adonis, or whether this is the more mature caring relationship of two people who can care for each other as separate human beings. For the more disturbed teenagers who still require continued inpatient treatment, it is unlikely that two patients can give each other the kind of emotional growth experience they both need. Frequently such a "love" relationship between patients is based more on the mutual sharing of sickness or rebellion. Environmental anger, anxiety, and rejection merely cements the relationship firmer. Heterosexual relationships which arise within a hospital setting too often become the focus for unhealthy incestuous, aggressive, or psychotic behavior. Treatment personnel at all professional levels must beware lest they measure heterosexual patient relationships only on the basis of staff projections and expectations. Frequently, the need on the part of the staff to see a patient as adolescent, as mature, or as "well" tends to blind otherwise sensitive therapeutic personnel to the infantile, self-centered, or grossly disturbed aspects of this relationship between patients. Sometimes the staff's need to be rid of a disturbing patient pushes this patient into an otherwise untherapeutic friendship. If the members of the treatment team really believe that the adolescent patient is ready and capable of entering into a meaningful, continued heterosexual relationship, they should question closely why this particular adolescent is still in the hospital setting. If he is capable of a mature love relationship, it is unlikely that the teenager belongs in an inpatient environment. If indeed the teenager does require inpatient treatment because of his emotional weaknesses, it is unlikely that he can sustain a mutually beneficial heterosexual relationship with another patient. On the other hand a "love" relationship with a healthy member of the community outside the hospital environment may provide a profound emotional growth stimulus for the disturbed teenager who has the capability for growth.

Such an ongoing continued evaluation process involving everything the adolescent patient does and does not do is both enriching and emotionally wearing for all members of the treatment team. In this diagnostic and treatment process, therapeutic personnel are obliged to use their own reactions and intuitions as valid diagnostic cues. Such total treatment involvement requires a high level of individual integrity and personal strength in every member of the treatment personnel. If the caring staff is willing and able to maintain this intensive treatment investment, they can form with the adolescent patient a powerful therapeutic force.

Chapter IV

The Principles of Residential Treatment

THE THERAPEUTIC ALLIANCE

In all their interactions with the disturbed adolescent, the therapeutic staff must maintain the constantly clear principle that they are allied with the adolescent patient, in a relationship designed to his maximum advantage. If the treatment team are comfortable with this identity as the patient's ally, they can then more easily refuse to be set up by the disturbed teenager as an opponent or as an enemy. Many hurt and sensitive adolescents would feel more comfortable dealing with those around them as enemies because enemies can be reacted against and kept at a distance. Allies and friends may come uncomfortably close, close enough to hurt and close enough to see clearly how uncertain and how inadequate the teenager may be. The adolescent must learn during the treatment process that the therapeutic staff respect him as a human being, as an individual, and as a person with assets. In the treatment setting the teenager should never be allowed to lose the sense of respect which is an ever present goal toward growth and maturity. The teenager in the residential setting should be consistently faced with the total environmental expectation that he will grow and mature to his fullest potential; it is the duty of the treating staff to help him in his growth and development to the level of his maximum individual capability (Alderton, 1965).

This treating-training process with the disturbed adolescent is slow, uncertain, and at times singularly unrewarding both

61

for the patient and for the members of the therapeutic team. Because they are concerned, the caring staff and the teenage patient may periodically feel angry and frustrated and are likely to vent their dissatisfactions on each other. It is essential for the team members to remember that, because they care, they are liable to be frustrated and disappointed. Even more important, they must be constantly aware of how frustrated the teenage patient becomes when all his genuine efforts produce so little immediate benefit or gratification. Even at these times of maximum frustration and anger, the treatment team must remember that they are the allies to the patient and that they must express their anger in a fashion that does not in any way hurt him. Because caring staff are frustrated, they must take care lest they taunt the patient with the fact that he does not have a key, that he is sick, or that he is in some way incompetent. Where staff members struggle with their own hopes for the patient and with their own counteridentifications with these teenagers, they may try to stimulate and to force the adolescent to grow and to mature by pointing out his inadequacies and his inconsistencies in an angry humiliating fashion. In their resentment at the inevitably slow progress, treatment team members may loudly proclaim their own competency because they have white coats, the personal freedom to come and go, and the privilege of driving cars. It is thus imperative that the treatment staff have an awareness of this anger and the reasons for their frustration, so that they can avoid giving vent to their disappointments in a fashion that hurts the patient or undermines the strength of the treatment team.

A mature sense of humor requires a great deal of emotional strength and flexibility. The adolescent who has been admitted to an inpatient setting is usually lacking in personal integrity, and therefore cannot understand or use staff "joking" in a therapeutic growth-producing fashion. To understand jokes, to appreciate humor, and to enjoy teasing, the teenager must be able to tolerate unreality and to enjoy fantasy. The adolescent inpatient has too little solid reality contact to give himself the freedom of fantasy. He is still too uncertain of his own emotional integration to enjoy fantasied disintegration. When a teenager is able meaningfully to enjoy age-appropriate jokes, he is usually ready for discharge from the inpatient setting.

Whether the teenage patient admits this reality or not, the treatment team members provide the identification models for the adolescent patient's behavior. This may be a negative model which the patient has to defy or it may be a positive model which a teenager strives to emulate. In the therapeutic alliance with the patient, the staff member must consistently maintain a relationship toward the patient based on mutual self-respect—a model whereby the adolescent can learn to respect himself and those around him. These disturbed adolescents come to the hospital environment with their self-confidence badly shattered. By the very nature of their illness which required hospitalization, their ego strength is already uncertain; for all adolescents, the added fact of psychiatric hospitalization is a tremendous additional blow to their self-respect.

"Everyone looks on us as 'sickies.' When we go into a room, they expect us to rant and to rave. Sometimes I think they do not even feel we are human."

These words of a 16 year old girl describe the way in which she felt her schoolmates regarded her in the public school setting. Though some of these comments are reality based, she was describing also her own feelings as she projected these emotions on to her environment. Following his hospital admission, the adolescent feels with justification that he has been judged by society and by his family as being inadequate, incompetent, and in some way bad. Though he may vehemently deny that there is any justification for such an evaluation, in his very private thoughts he himself wonders whether he is indeed totally incompetent and completely unloveable.

"You will never know what it does to a guy to be put in the Zoo like this. He doesn't like to think about it but he often wonders whether he is crazy. My folks use to tell me that no one could love me and sometimes I wonder if they were right. Perhaps I am completely bad. Perhaps I would be better dead. Maybe I should have killed myself and rid this world of something evil. Still, I don't need to kill myself—my parents did it for me—they threw me into this hospital."

With such uncertain self-confidence and such undermined personal security, these disturbed teenagers are acutely aware of their vulnerability to be hurt and of their basic need for ego strengthening and support. Since they fear so much that they will be wounded by the very people who are supposed to care for them—as they have been wounded by caring people in the past—they try to stabilize their environment by provoking the treating personnel into rejecting and into fighting with them from the time of their admission. In this way the adolescent can establish a precarious stability and certainty to his environment. He can set up again the kind of environment to which he has become accustomed in the past. If he has everyone hating him, he does not need to beware lest he be hurt by someone who is supposed to care for him. When everyone is his enemy and no one is his ally, he can maintain a constant emotional barrier and protect himself from being wounded again. If he really did believe that a caring person was his ally, he might then tend to lower his emotional barriers and thus become more vulnerable to being hurt. The natural understandable tendency with the newly admitted adolescent patient is to set up protective emotional barriers and to define the staff members as enemies, not as allies. The treating personnel must take care to avoid perpetuating this unhealthy distance barrier. If the caring staff insist on viewing themselves always as the patient's ally and on acting at all times as the teenager's supporter and friend, it becomes much more difficult for the adolescent to maintain this barrier between himself and the outside world. In the face of constant staff respect and solicitude, the disturbed teenager finds it increasingly impossible to deny to himself that he wants to care and be cared for; if the treatment team uniformly acts as allies to the adolescent patient, at some stage of the treatment process he will be tempted to trust. In any setting the teenage

64

patient can only trust other people if first he trusts himself enough to trust. Before he can trust himself, he must have the beginnings of self-confidence. In the treatment setting, a constant therapeutic alliance between the patient and the staff team is the first and the most essential treatment process in helping these teenagers to develop more self-confidence, more ego strengths, and more mastery ability. Unless the treatment team sincerely believe that they are indeed the patient's allies under all circumstances, meaningful growth-producing treatment cannot exist.

The Tasks of the Therapeutic Alliance

While the residential team is constantly the ally of the adolescent patient, the first treatment task in promoting emotional growth and therapeutic movement is to make the teenage patient's behavior his responsibility and his struggle rather than the responsibility or the struggle of the people in his environment. The second growth-promoting task of the residential team is to supplement the adolescent patient's emotional strengths as much as he needs to assist him in handling this responsibility task and to help him grow to greater emotional strengths, to more acceptable patterns of behavior, and eventually to personal gratification in his continued growth and maturity. The third residential task is to teach and to train the teenage patient in the most appropriate, individual ways of coping and in the best directions for his maximum growth. The fourth and at times the most difficult growth and treatment task in the residential setting is to support the adolescent patient in leaving the hospital environment when his emotional growth and his personality capability have made such a separation appropriate and necessary.

THE ILLNESS IS THE PATIENT'S RESPONSIBILITY

The typical adolescent patient who comes to long-term hospital treatment has evolved a life-long pattern of behavior whereby almost everyone in his environment has struggled more over his behavior than has he himself. When these young men and women are admitted to an inpatient setting, automatically they try once more to make those around them battle with their behavior. Classically, the disturbed adolescent who expresses his inner anxieties and turmoil in action uses this ploy soonest and with more conscious deliberation than any other patient group:

"I don't like your food. I don't like your place. Unless you send me home I won't eat a bite!" To this challenge to this attempt to make the staff struggle, the response is easy—"Fine, if you do not eat, we shall send the food back to the kitchen. You are going to be very hungry, and we do not want you to be hungry—but it is your stomach and your decision."

Equally easy to handle in the residential setting is the teenager who insists on wearing the most outlandish clothes, the most bedraggled beard, or the most disheveled hair style, and who loudly trumpets his appearance as being absolutely unchangeable. The treatment staff refuse to be set up as rejecting enemies but at the same time they cannot allow the teenager to hurt himself or to be hurt. They would certainly be unhappy about placing the adolescent in a position where he would be exposed to community ridicule. Thus, to protect the patient, it is required that he remain in the residential unit for as long as he maintains such styles—for weeks, months, or years if necessary. This treatment support of course means that there will be no outside movies, no community dates and no town trips, but then, as the adolescent's ally, the prime concern of the treatment team is to prevent his being an object of scorn. In the hospital setting it is alright to maintain his weird appearance, for a hospital is a place for weird people. His behavior is his final personal responsibility but the treating staff will ally themselves with the self-respecting part of his personality to insure that he does not make himself ridiculous to those around him or, in the long run, to himself.

The patient's behavior becomes his responsibility when he is given rewards consistent only with his demonstrated level of capability. The teenage patient is accepted exactly at the level he presents himself. If he acts in a childlike fashion, he is accepted as a child and is given the responsibilities and the privileges of a child. The treatment team members respect him as a child and value him as a child. This is not an angry approach but is realistically based on warmth, sincerity, and acceptance. The adolescent is not expected to do more than he is capable of but, equally, he is not given unrealistic rewards which he has not earned. Too often in his everyday living the disturbed adolescent has been able to act at an infantile or childlike level, yet glean the rewards of adolescent maturity. Under these circumstances, the pressure for increased competency and for more mature behavior was minimal. Frequently an infantile pattern of behavior was perpetuated and encouraged. Where childlike responsibility only is given for childlike behavior, there is less reinforcement for this infantile behavior. Where the treating staff, without anxiety and without anger, give approval based only on the patient's demonstrated level of functioning, there is less negative reinforcement of the patient's anxiety. The teenage patient has before him a positive consistent model of comfortable adult acceptance rather than the negative models he had in the past, where his disruptive behavior goaded his parents and family to react in uncontrolled fury at his uncontrolled behavior; no longer does environmental anger and anxiety make the adolescent even more anxious so that he acts in an increasingly disruptive fashion.

Sure I got thrown out of class today. Sure I threatened to slug Mary. So what! Why can't I go out tonight?
(Why not indeed?) Well, if the small classroom was so upsetting to you and if your emotional fuse was so short that you almost lost control, obviously then you are in no shape to leave the hospital grounds. It might be much too upsetting out there at a movie. You might feel like slugging someone.

The teenage patient's behavior is accepted exactly at the level at which he presents it. The message is read in the way he delivers it. If the teenager is indeed acting in a fashion which shows that he has only childlike capabilities, it is a most angry and most punitive action to expect him to take adolescent or adult responsibilities. By everything they do, the disturbed adolescent patients tell the treating personnel what they are capable of doing and how much responsibility they can handle. In their main role as the patient's ally, the caring staff must accept these communications and respect the teenage patient on the basis of what he has communicated. At times, because of their own emotional needs and investments, treatment team members may need to see the disturbed adolescent as much less sick than he really is. In such instances, regressed or infantile behavior may be ignored and the adolescent pushed and encouraged into activities and responsibilities for which he is not yet ready. In these situations, the therapeutic results may be most disruptive. If he is accepted at the level of his teenage braggadocio rather than on the basis of his demonstrated infantile level of coping, the more disturbed adolescent may be placed in a situation where the demands on him are far beyond his ego capabilities with resultant personality disruption and emotional regression.

"Life is not fair" is a repeated proclamation by the adolescent patient. Somehow such protestations are supposed to wring great sympathy from the listener and often staff members struggle over this unfair reality of the teenage patient. No one needs to deny that life has not been fair to these young men and young women but life rarely is fair in the rewards and the punishments we receive. If these disturbed and disturbing adolescents had received "fair" treatment for their past behavior, in the words of Hamlet (Act II, Scene II) ". . . use every man after his desert, and who should 'scape whipping?" While many of these teenagers have not received a fair share of life's bounty, equally they have missed the fair responsibility for their past behavior. It is not the task of treating personnel to try to compensate for past unfairness (Inglis, 1963) but rather to help the adolescent to a fair share in the future, based on his responsible behavior. It is impossible and totally unrealistic for the treatment team to try to make up for what the adolescent has missed in his growing years. The therapeutic personnel must value what they can give to the patient during his stay in the hospital. As the patient's ally, they can provide him with a rich, meaningful growth experience in the present but they cannot relive the past. The task of the residence is to help the adolescent to the maximum future gratification. When the adolescent finds that consistent behavior is expected from him and that he will be given responsibilities and privileges only at the level at which he functions, higher functioning and better social adaptation become more of a necessity and more of a goal—and eventually more rewarding in themselves (Hendrickson and Holmes, 1959).

There is little the adolescent patient can do to place his responsibility elsewhere when, in the warmest most emphatic fashion, the child-care workers states to him,

> Gee, you must have had a rough day. Here, you had to throw water at George and cuss Mrs. Smith. Let's you and I take it easy tonight—no going off the unit until you feel more relaxed. Just put your feet up and take it easy.

The teenage patient knows, or soon learns, that behind such a gentle unanxious approach is the constant firm reminder that the adolescent himself is responsible for his own behavior and that, to be given responsibilities, he needs to maintain an appropriate, consistently responsible level of behavior. No staff member struggles. None of the caring team is angry. If the teenage patient acts childishly and irresponsibly, it is the most natural thing to accept him and to respect him as being childish and irresponsible—and in no way eligible to receive the rewards or the burdens of maturity and of adolescent responsibility. Acceptance and alliance are the key words in the treatment of the adolescent but this therapeutic bond is formed at the level of demonstrated emotional capability which the teenager shows.

If the adolescent patient is able to make his behavior the struggle of the treatment staff members, the patient's actions are then likely to become even more unsettling and his anxiety more disruptive to himself and to those around him. For many of these disturbed adolescents, their disruptive behavior is a conditioned response to inner anxiety. Where the treatment team members respond to the teenager's disorganized and disorganizing behavior by themselves acting angrily and disruptively, the adolescent patient is made even more anxious and thus more liable to act out his tensions by further disruptiveness. His conditioned behavior patterns are further reinforced by the staff example of anxiety-driven behavior. This vicious circle of negative reinforcement can only be broken when the treatment team members see themselves constantly as the patient's ally and as accepting him always at his level of functioning.

Certain patterns of patient behavior such as the self-mutilation incidents described by Offer and Barglow (1960) are especially prone to make treatment team members angry, anxious, and confused. Even in the face of such profoundly aggressive patient behavior, there should be absolutely no alteration in the certainty and the stability of the staff treatment approach. Even under these circumstances the adolescent patient is responsible for his or her behavior and is accepted at the level he or she demonstrates. If the teenage girl cuts or hurts herself, then she has obviously shown that she has only limited capability for handling responsibility. For weeks, months, or years, this adolescent girl can be maintained at a level of minimum responsibility, in an environment stripped of potential cutting or stress-producing instruments. She is thus accepted at the very regressed level she has demonstrated. In this treatment alliance, the caring staff members cannot allow her to hurt herself. She lives in a protective environment for as long as she demonstrates that she is unable to protect herself. No treatment team member need struggle individually nor accept as a personal attack the very aggressive, punitive aspect of such symptoms. If the adolescent girl has even a modicum of ego strength, eventually she will find such a sheltered, monotonous existence tedious and unrewarding; then, and only then, she may find it worthwhile to strive toward more mature behavior where she can handle increased responsibility, including the personal responsibility not to hurt herself. There are of course certain very disturbed adolescents who do not have adequate ego strength to refrain from hurting themselves and from hurting others; these teenagers also must be accepted at their level of functioning and, if need be, maintained in a controlled protective environment for the rest of their lives. This control and protection is always based on realistic respect for the adolescent's individual capabilities and on the treatment alliance with the teenage patient.

"You know I'll be miserable if you pull me out of school. You surely don't want me to like you, if you do a thing like that."

Where the treatment team members do care for a teenage patient and do wish him to succeed, frequently the disturbed adolescent will test to see whether the treatment staff wish him to succeed for their personal gratification or for his own benefit. The adolescent will thus pick a cherished staff project in which the teenager is involved and will test to see which is more important to the staff members—the project or the adolescent. Where the treatment team have worked long and hard to place a teenager in public school, as a testing device this adolescent may show disruptive behavior to see whether it is more important that he be maintained in public school for staff gratification or whether he can be given the support he requires by being pulled back into the hospital setting. It is frequently the case with these adolescents that in the past they were expected to achieve not for their own benefit but to please someone else —parents saw their children as narcissistic extensions rather than as growing individuals. When the adolescent patient has tested repeatedly and is sure that his success is valued in terms of his personal achievement and his individual gratification, and not for the staff's narcissistic emotional needs, then his behavior remains his responsibility but is also a potential source of gratification. The aim of the residential team is not to be liked, but rather to be respected as secure, meaningful, dependable adults, adults who can then be used as consistent identification models.

71

Early one morning a 15 year old adolescent boy slipped the following note under the office door of his unit doctor.

Dear Dr. E.,
   I feel like running away at 10:55 a.m. through the front door. What should you do?

                                        Signed
                                        Walt.

Fifteen minutes later the doctor slipped his note under the door of the patient's room.

Dear Walt,
   When you decide whether you have to run away past my office door, let me know—then I will decide what to do about your responsibility.

                                        Signed
                                        Doctor E.

P.S. What are you running away from?"

Walter struggled but he did not run.

It is neither the treatment function nor the therapeutic purpose of the residential unit team to become part of the psychotic world of the psychotic adolescent. Rather it is hoped that the psychotic teenager be encouraged to enter or re-enter and subsequently adapt himself to the ordinary world. As mentioned previously, the psychotic patient has made his craziness the struggle of those around him. If he set fires, it was his parents, his peers, and his neighbors who had to contend with them. They may have done nothing about his disruptive behavior because he was "sick" and consequently they felt powerless, anxious, or angry; sometimes they reacted violently, beat or abused him unmercifully, and locked him away—feeling guilty, anxious, and confused over the strength of their anger and the force of their impulses. The anxiety, the guilt, and the rejection of the people in his environment made the psychotic adolescent even more anxious so that he tended to act even more crazily with an even higher environmental tension. As long as the other people struggled over his behavior and its effects to a greater degree than did the psychotic teenager, the more the patient's illness was perpetuated in a cycle of reinforcement. His psychotic behavior patterns became increasingly fixed as a method of expressing anxiety, as a means of controlling his environment, and as a sure way of gaining attention, albeit painful and anxious attention.

> Jerry started barking after dinner. We tried to get him to stop but he kept on barking. So we all barked back at him. We must have kept it up for over an hour, the whole unit barking.

As these nursing notes describe, the behavior of this psychotic adolescent on the small residential unit resulted in the whole unit's becoming an integral part of his psychosis. The teenage patient's illness ran the treatment unit as it had run his past environment thereby giving him little reason and less support for changing his psychotic behavior. Insofar as he controlled his environment, he was the center of attention; the treatment personnel, his potential identification models, were apparently acting as crazily as he was. His illness was thus perpetuated and accentuated. When the treatment staff began to ignore Jerry's barking and when they indicated to him that, if he functioned as an animal, he would be given the minimum level of responsibility and privilege one would give to an animal, his barking ceased and his direct communication began and has increased ever since. When the environmental craziness and anxiety subsided, the patient's inner confusion and psychosis could be reduced.

> I got so mad at his dirty, smelly floor that I took a mop, gripped it in his hands and forced him to clean up the mess. I had to force him but we sure cleaned up that room.

By urinating on his bedroom floor, this psychotic 14 year old adolescent boy eventually so perturbed and enraged the child-care worker who wrote the above note that the latter could no longer tolerate the situation—thus the patient's behavior became solely the problem of the child-care worker. Even after the episode described above, the patient again urinated on his floor that evening. This time, however, he was told that a mop and a bucket were available to him should he want to clean up his mess. During the course of the next day he urinated repeatedly on the floor. The staff took pains to avoid any outward signs of dismay—it was the teenager's room, his mess, and his smell. Two days later the young man requested the mop and the water, thoroughly cleaned his stinking room, and never again urinated on the floor. At least this part of his behavior had become his own problem. Outside support, in this case in the shape of a mop and a bucket, was available to help him deal with the problem but the basic responsibility for his behavior was his alone. This teenage patient could be asked to take this level of social responsibility because he had shown in his other areas of functioning that he was able to handle a high level of responsibility. He was very competently attending the hospital school on a full-time basis and taking an active part in all hospital athletic activities. Patients should not be required to assume more responsibility than they can tolerate. If this 14 year old teenager had been profoundly regressed in all areas of behavior so that urinating on his bedroom floor was merely one part of a general pattern of primitive infantile behavior, he would have been accepted at this very regressed level and if necessary he would have been fed and diapered like an infant.

The severely neurotic patient also makes his behavior the struggle and the responsibility of those around him:

Though John was socially competent and academically most able in his public school setting, each morning found the school bus waiting for him because he simply could not get dressed in time. The bus waited, the other teenage patients fretted and became restless, the residential staff were anxious that this 15 year old boy would miss the school bus and thus his very important public school involvement—in short, everyone struggled over his behavior except the patient. He continued to take 40 minutes to button his shirt. Since he had shown that he had definite personality strengths which he could use very capably in other areas, the full responsibility for this bizarre dressing behavior could be placed on his shoulders. John was told by the treatment team leader that a different approach was about to be taken. The various possibilities were discussed with him. If the school bus arrived on time and he was not ready, should the bus leave without him? If he missed school, the staff would obviously consider that he needed more time for study to keep up with his school work. Naturally, since he was unable to go to school, it would be reasonable to decide that he was equally unable to go on any other off-campus activities. Since he took so much time to dress, would it be better for him to go to bed earlier so that he could rise at an early hour and be dressed in time. Thus since he did take 40 minutes to put on his shirt, perhaps he should get up 40 minutes sooner.

The treatment staff work with the teenage patients to give them whatever strength and support they need but on every occasion the final responsibility for the patient's behavior belongs to the patient. If the young man just discussed had not been functioning well in his general social interactions, the treatment staff would have taken his obvious compulsiveness as a sign that perhaps he should be given less responsibility. The treatment team would have considered whether it would be beneficial if he were withdrawn from the public school setting, placed in the hospital school once more, and given increased support over the next few months so that he could augment his ego strength and eventually return later to a public school setting. In a similar treatment pattern, the anxious fearful patient is accepted totally as he presents himself. His inadequacies are met without anger and without reproach but the treatment staff feel free to raise questions as to whether he should go home if he is so very anxious and so very worried. As his allies they can wonder openly whether it is really best that he go to public school or to an off-campus movie if he is as sensitive as he suggests and acts.

The treatment team members must refuse to be set up as antagonists to the adolescent patient. To the teenagers' singing "We Shall Overcome," the therapeutic staff inquire solicitously as to how they can help the patients "overcome" to the maximum benefit of the teenagers themselves. While the residential team is a constant ally of all patients, an early lesson that all teenage patients must learn is the reality that emotional pain and personal conflict do not absolve them from individual responsibility for their behavior. Very often the adolescent patient will announce loudly and well in advance that, since he is suffering or since he is in some kind of emotional agony, he is about to show disruptive or irresponsible behavior (Holmes, 1964, p. 89; Redl and Wineman, 1957, p. 261).

> I think I will get drunk tonight. Betty is not here and, God, I just feel empty!

In these words, a 16 year old young man tried to proclaim that loneliness in some way should allow him to indulge in nonproductive alcoholic excesses. In the treatment process he had to learn that he would be held fully responsible for his behavior should he try to drown his sorrows in alcohol. He needed to face the fact that his retreat into drinking was an emotional defense that not only kept him lonely but also allowed him to avoid the reality of his deep personal insecurity and loneliness—a handicap that, with support, he could overcome. In the residential unit he had to learn that he could develop an increasing ability to relieve his loneliness by reaching out to members of the treatment team, the peer group, and, if he wanted, to his family. He had to learn that he could lighten some of the pain of his loneliness through academic and physical work and, in this fashion, not only relieve the pain to some degree but also increase his capability and self-confidence. Conflict and pain are not acceptable excuses in general society or in a residential treatment unit for irresponsible behavior, for physical attacks, for abuse based on racial or religious prejudice, or for not working.

The adolescent patient's sick behavior is his individual way of handling his inner tensions and uncertainties. Throughout his developmental years, his illness has been perpetuated by the secondary gains he derived from being ill—the rewards of being infantile and irresponsible, the pleasure of seeing everyone else become uncomfortable, and the gratification of omnipotence. If the residential treatment team can make this illness, this inefficient pattern of coping, the struggle and the responsibility of the teenage patient, such behavior becomes much less rewarding; the disturbed adolescent then has to face his underlying basic anxieties much more directly when he has the full responsibility for his actions. As the treatment team works toward the goal of giving the patient full responsibility for his behavior, they must at the same time show him better ways to deal with his underlying tensions. The caring staff must support the teenage patient with all necessary environmental strength and direction so that his inner uncertainties can be better controlled and eventually channelled toward personality growth.

Residential Support for the Teenage Patient

In the life of the adolescent patient before his admission to the residential setting, usually the most consistent factor has been environmental inconsistency. In inpatient treatment, constant environmental stability must be maintained (Worden, 1951). Sameness, consistency, permanence—monotonously from one day to the next—is essential. In his daily living the disturbed adolescent needs to know what is dependable. He has learned from past bitter experience that what seemed secure and certain in his environment was not really reliable or predictable. Under stress, sometimes the stress provoked by his demands and his anxieties, he has found that the stability of his environment was too easily shattered. He has thus learned to expect inconsistency, betrayal, and attack from those who say they seek his trust and wish to care for him. In the residential unit, the teenage patient will naturally mistrust the security and the stability of those around him. Basic trust cannot be expected from the disturbed adolescent patient for an extended period after his admission. He will need to test and retest to discover whether the environmental structures and reactions are certain and dependable. The adolescent patient who proclaims that he trusts the treatment staff soon after his admission is, consciously or unconsciously, already testing the stability and the reality of the treatment team. If the therapeutic personnel, because of their own needs, allow themselves to believe that this hurt adolescent genuinely trusts them after all the painful experiences he has lived through, they will in reality have been seduced and undermined by his illness. That teenage patients do not trust and cannot trust at the time of their admission is a reality which treating personnel need not take personally. The therapeutic staff cannot reasonably be trusted by the adolescent patient until he has tested and thereby proved their trustworthiness to himself.

For a residential treatment unit it is necessary to have certain fixed rules of functioning which indicate clearly individual and group freedoms and responsibilities. Most adolescent treatment centers have definite, established levels of patient responsibility which are widely known amongst the patients and the treating staff. These clearly delineated levels of expected responsibility help provide environmental certainty and security. If an adolescent patient knows that a specific level of behavior will definitely bring him a known responsibility, this understanding gives him a constant security with which he can deal. The teenage patient can strive toward this official status with an appreciation of the level of responsibility and the burden of anxiety he is seeking. If he is sure that childlike behavior will bring a more childlike level of responsibility, he can with this certainty of environmental stability make an emotional decision concerning his preferred level of functioning. His inner struggle is then more focused on his personal emotional conflicts rather than on any instability in his environment.

Within a residential treatment unit, acceptable and unacceptable patterns of interacting must be definitely delineated. When the adolescent patient knows that direct physical aggression is not tolerated under any circumstances as a method of expression, he can deal more comfortably with this established certainty and devote his energies to handling his personal anxieties and angers more appropriately. The teenage patient needs to learn that the reasonable, socially acceptable expression of anger is tolerable and indeed welcome in the residential environment but that physical violence is unacceptable both in the inpatient setting and in normal social groups. Under no circumstances is abuse based on religious or racial grounds tolerated in an inpatient unit. The teenager learns in a most definite and consistent fashion that no one, either patient or staff, will be allowed to become a social scapegoat due to his religious or ethnic origin. Unreasonable, prejudiced anger or anxiety is not allowed to be acted out destructively in any therapeutic setting.

Whatever behavioral expectations are placed on the adolescent patients must also be placed on the treating staff. Within the inpatient residential unit the entire environmental expectation is toward individual growth and increasing maturity. Personal regression may be tolerated and understood but the sick adolescent knows constantly that rewards are not given for sickness. If he regresses, his regressed behavior is viewed sympathetically, at times with much pity, but definitely not with encouragement. If teenage patients are to be taught that physical violence is a totally unacceptable form of emotional expression, the treating staff must also demonstrate this expectation. The adolescent patients require the assuredness that physical attack on any patient by any staff member is cause for immediate dismissal. This policy does not mean of course that a staff member should not protect himself or protect other people from a physical attack but it does mean that, under no circumstances, does a member of the treatment team initiate physical violence. In the same vein, racial and religious prejudices cannot be tolerated from nor acted out in any fashion by members of the treatment team. If a basic pattern of behavior is correct for the adolescent, such basic concepts are also obviously correct for members of the treatment team. If the caring personnel expect to receive respect from the adolescent, they must demonstrate their own self-respect and must show the adolescent that he is respected.

Staff members at all professional levels, when they start working in a residential treatment center, may have the need to delve into the teenage patient's past to achieve some deep "understanding." Most disturbed teenagers will cooperate gladly in such mutual wallowing so that they can in this way avoid dealing with their present reality.

> After Chuck broke the window, I took him to his room. He was very upset. He told me in detail how his mother used to beat him for breaking things at home. We had a very meaningful discussion for over an hour. I think I understand Chuck much better now.

Perhaps the nurse who wrote this note did "understand" Chuck much better but somehow Chuck, with all this discussion, avoided facing the reality that he had just broken a window. An understanding of the past is very stimulating and enriching for treatment purposes if this understanding is used. Frequently, however, the disturbed adolescent can seduce staff members into a pseudounderstanding based on past experiences and former trauma but with little understanding of present reality. In this incident described, the nurse, rather than reveling so completely in past anxieties, should have used the understanding gained from the teenager's conversation to face Chuck with the reality of the broken window. While she empathized with the teenager's past anxieties and insecurities, the nurse should have wondered along with the teenager why he still had to act in his present unproductive fashion. The nurse could have discussed with Chuck how he might have more effectively dealt with his inner tensions rather than break windows. Furthermore, she could have considered with the adolescent why he had to act in so self-destructive a manner while beginning to plan with the boy an alternative method of handling his tensions. The nurse could have pointed out to Chuck the punitive and painful environmental reaction his past behavior had produced, the angers and the anxieties his window breaking once more aroused, and the very self-destructive result from such antisocial behavior. The main focus of residential treatment is on the day-to-day living, the reality of the here and now and the problem of coping with this present reality. In inpatient treatment, the past is past and the future may be; the treatment task is to live with optimum efficiency in the present. Many teenage patients repeatedly dredge up the past to excuse their present but such an excuse is not valid in residential living. The treatment team understand the pain of the teenager's past, his earlier uncertainties and loneliness, but such pain is not a valid excuse for refusing to try in the present. The caring personnel can understand why the adolescent fears and reacts to his inner anxieties but, based on the present reality and on the stability of his treatment environment, they expect him to try again and, hopefully, this time to have a different living experience. If the adolescent patient does learn to cope with his present situation, his future will take care of itself.

It is necessary for many teenage patients to test the inpatient treatment setting in order to see whether or not it can be manipulated or pressured by their parents. So often in their past, these adolescents have found that the anxieties, the angers, and the confusions of caring parental people tended to undermine the usual sources of social strength and stability. Some parents, worried about the disruptive behavior of their disturbed adolescent, so threatened and manipulated the school authorities that the adolescent did not know what he could depend on in school. Previous therapists and counselors have been so badgered and pressured by uncertain, angry parents that they eventually rejected the teenager. In their need for strong secure support, many anxious parents have tended to depreciate sensitive, empathic people who offered less support than they needed. The adolescent inpatients need to know that their parents have delegated the parental responsibility to the treating staff and will support the treatment purpose of the therapeutic personnel. Frequently the adolescent patient will test the residential integrity by trying to play his parents off against the treatment unit as he used to play one parent against the other. While he loudly complains about the residential expectation that he shower each day, the young man will state that his mother never bothered if he did not shower every day. The staff answer to such comments is that, though they respect the wishes of his mother in his home setting, the teenager is faced with the reality that he must live up to the expectations of his present living environment. He is helped to appreciate that a reasonable social rule can be maintained in face of anxieties and pressures. Where there is a definite residential policy that clothes should be purchased only at a reasonable expense level, the teenager may proclaim "My folks have plenty money and won't mind if I buy $15.00 shirts. In fact, Dad told me to get them."—to this point, the adolescent is told firmly but gently that he is still expected to live within the residential unit limitations. The treatment staff are sure that an understanding supporting parent who is aware of the purpose of such residential structures, would support this price limit. In this fashion the treatment staff ally themselves with the emotional strengths of the parenting figures in the patient's background. While the adolescent patients are allowed and encouraged to individualize their clothing, they must be trained to keep clothes expenses within reasonable social limits. An expense ceiling prevents any competition to see which teenager can sport the fanciest or the most expensive clothing. A spending limitation stops the teenager from deliberately attacking his parents by running up clothing bills. Such limits help insure that the teenage patients are wearing clothes that are generally similar to those worn in the community outside the hospital, the community in which the adolescent will eventually have to be accepted as he moves toward a healthier more productive social adjustment.

For the disturbed adolescent, the residential unit should provide human relationships, security, and stability. In this inpatient living, these teenagers need to experience the treating staff as human beings, as men and women who can face their own feelings and can deal with these feelings constructively. In their developmental years before hospital admission, these adolescents had repeatedly encountered adults and peers who were afraid of or who could not control their own emotions; they have known parents, relatives, and friends who denied or who ran from feelings too strong or too primitive, either in themselves or in the teenage patient. In day-to-day residential living, these young men and women need to have consistent relationships with staff who are human beings and who can reasonably and constructively be warm and happy, angry and sad in situations where such feelings are appropriate and meaningful. These adolescents must have the repeated inpatient living experience of being with people who can face their own limitations and the reality that periodically they themselves fail and make mistakes. Through such relationship experiences, the disturbed adolescent can find that, for most people, a mistake need not be shattering or irretrievable. They can learn that even though people have weaknesses, they also have strengths which enable them to cope and grow in constructive ways.

In a stable, warm therapeutic environment, it is necessary for the treatment team members to gauge just how much external support the adolescent patient does need and how much individual anxiety he can tolerate. At all times the teenage patient is accepted as he is with his personal strengths and individual limitations. Though he is expected to face the responsibility for his total behavior, he is given all the external support he needs to handle his impulses, to make his needs bearable, and to help him function productively. The psychotic adolescent is accepted at the level of his very fragile ego status and consistently given the maximum staff support as he tries to cope with his underlying emotional turmoil. This necessary external support and strengthening can be largely provided through consistent environmental directions and structures. The more uncertain, confused adolescent may require constant staff supervision on a one-to-one basis where a treatment member is with the adolescent at all times, providing ever-present external support and direction. Where the young patient has greater strength, he may be able to function with reasonable competence as a member of a small group for whom support is provided by the treatment staff. If the adolescent patient has the emotional capability, he may be allowed the responsibility and the burden of making his own limited decisions in certain clearly specified areas of social interaction. As the adolescent begins to try his own strength, he may be permitted the freedom of the hospital grounds without direct physical staff supervision. When he is emotionally stronger and better integrated, he may be able to make town trips on his own. Each level of patient responsibility and staff support must be clearly defined and based on the needs of the individual patient.

As the adolescent patient becomes emotionally stronger and better integrated, he does not require direct staff support but carries with him the introjected assurance of such support. It is a delicate treatment art to provide consistent outside strengthening without making the emancipating patient feel that he is being controlled. The treatment staff must give the adolescent patient the support and the certainty that they will encourage his strength and respect his limitations. They do not demand that he function beyond his capability but they expect him to try at a reasonable level. When the young patient knows that the treatment staff will support his considered decision to withdraw from public school if his inner tensions become unmanageable, he frequently finds that it becomes unnecessary to withdraw. He is more confident that he does not need to allow his anxiety to build up explosively in school since he can withdraw to a more protected environment if he finds it necessary; often then he neither has to withdraw nor explode. With the assuredness of staff support carried with him constantly, part of his anxiety burden is relieved. If, however, the young man were to act consistently in an infantile fashion, he would be accepted at this regressed level of emotional functioning; treatment staff members would move actively to lower the demands placed on him and would provide external support necessary for such an infantile level of competence—under these circumstances, it would be totally unreasonable to expect him to maintain himself in public school. Illness, childlike behavior, irresponsibility, and lack of complete control rather than resulting in rejection bring about staff acceptance of such outward expressions of emotional capability; on the basis of this treatment acceptance and understanding, therapeutic personnel provide all necessary outside strength and direction for the disturbed adolescent.

TEACHING AND TRAINING THE ADOLESCENT PATIENT

He is as phony as a three dollar bill. He parrots back to me what the other child-care workers say. He sounds as if he had learned a speech. He always was a good "con" man, and that's what he is now.

When the treatment team members ask these disturbed teen-agers to change their lifelong behavior patterns, they should not expect these adolescents to be expert in their new approach to people. Too frequently in a treatment setting, the therapeutic staff seem to think that these patients can be comfortable and expert in their new pattern or healthy behavior, patterns these adolescents do not really know or understand. As these young patients try to modify their previous way of living, realistically they have to imitate, realistically they are awkward and "phony." What they are trying is new and foreign to them; if they really did know how to cope and how to relate in a mature fashion, they would not require to be in an inpatient setting or involved in a treatment process. Though they might be experts at being sick, they are rank amateurs at showing appropriate, mature, and constructive behavior. As the adolescent tries to change, the experience of changing is a terrifying, nightmarish reality. As he gives up his illness and as he relinquishes his known emotional defenses, he feels naked, inadequate, and very sensitive; in reality at this stage in his emotional growth he is very vulnerable and could be easily hurt. The treatment team need to be aware of and to support this necessary transitional stage in the treatment progress of the teenager. As a 17 year old young man wrote:

THE MASK

Behind their phony mask they cower,
Waiting for the unknown hour
When they might try to pry
Their pretentious mask
And bask in the light of truth—

Oh how they attempt!
But they still remain unkempt,
While the truth await.

What a painful obsession it is,
When nothing else avails,
Pain all the more prevails—

Though they have failed,
They wish to be curtailed,
But the choice is theirs—

If and when they collide
This is one thing to abide,
That is; Thyself.
For the past journey was long and torturous
And so laborious.
So do not return by the road
Stand by your ground and
You will be crowned.

The disturbed adolescent has not had the usual social growth experiences, he has not developed the natural adolescent sensitivity and he does not have the normal age-appropriate flexibility. As these teenagers try to move into adolescent peer society, frequently they find that normal adolescents talk a different language from the language of sickness. For the disturbed teenager who has had to think only of himself, the society of adolescents who consider the feelings of other people may for him be a foreign territory.

"Man, I've lost my cool. I don't know what to do. I always knew what to do, but I can't do it any more. I've lost my cool so I'm just lost, lost man lost. You've got to help me!"

In a treatment setting it is necessary for the caring staff actually to train the teenager who is striving to change. This therapeutic training occurs at all levels of treatment relationships but most often and most effectively such training is carried out through the daily staff example, repeated over and over again, day after day. The treatment team train the adolescents in competent human functioning by personal example. Much necessary training can however be given by direct explicit coaching as is highlighted in the following child-care notes.

> Frank and I talked last night about dating. He wants to ask Margaret to go to a dance. We talked about how he could approach her in the dining room. I told him how we used to ask girls for dates when we were in high school. We discussed what he could say to her and how he might feel if she turned him down. He is scared that he will be shattered by a refusal but I pointed out to him how any growing adolescent has to live through such a disappointment.

> John is being teased in school. We talked tonight about how he could stand up to these boys and how he could avoid them in certain situations. As he considered the situation, it became obvious that he is setting himself up for teasing. I tried to illustrate to him how his behavior does invite such nasty comments and I suggested how better and how more appropriately he could behave. Afterwards, we went to the recreation room where we tried some boxing with the punching bag. John seemed to feel much better when he had worked out some of his tensions and anger on the bag.

> Meg was very upset tonight. Bill has really been giving her a rough time. We discussed how much she lets him push her around. She feels that she has no one else to care for her so she has to take it or she will lose him. I pointed out to her how much she is appreciated by the other girls on the unit and how much Mary especially looks up to her. I talked with her about making new acquaintances in her school club, in the school cafeteria, by going to dances and by possibly taking a job in town. She is very scared and uncertain on her own and will need a great deal of support.

Such child-care notes demonstrate how these teenagers can be helped very directly if the treatment staff are sensitive and attuned to the dilemma of these patients as they change and try new approaches. In the peer culture of the older adolescent, the teenagers find themselves too old to experiment and fail. When these older adolescents try to move from the hospital setting to associate with their community peer groups, they find the social groupings already established and themselves as outsiders. The normal junior high school student can more comfortably experiment and fail; he can be inadequate more easily because his age group is equally inept. Normally the older adolescent is expected to be past the age of such obvious personal and social inadequacy; he is supposed to have self-confidence and a security in his own capabilities. The sick adolescent, as he moves toward a healthier adjustment, does feel inadequate and is liable to feel these inadequacies repeatedly. As he looks around, he finds that his peer group is much further advanced in personal security and ability. In his uncertainty and his feeling of being different, he is alone and isolated and his natural tendency is to withdraw and to hide. In this necessary growth stage, the treatment personnel need to provide constant support and consistent direction in a fashion that the emancipating, growing teenager can tolerate. Any open discussion of his inadequacies may be both unbearable and unnecessary, but quietly and empathically the treatment team can provide cues and examples.

P—My allowance isn't any too rich nowadays!

T—So?

P—Well Doc, I wondered whether we could boost it a little—you know, give me a little freedom to do the things you say I should do. Like adding another three bucks so I can take Jenny to a movie.

T—Sounds reasonable—I guess she must be losing weight again. Three dollars sure won't give you much to eat if you both want to stop off for a Coke or a pizza, but three dollars is fine with me.

P—Say man, I forgot—she eats like a horse! I really didn't mean that! What about making that three dollars five? Remember, you suggested the idea, not me.

Thus the young adolescent is gently but firmly supported to a wider social experience. When later he does ask his girlfriend to go with him for a hamburger after a movie, it will now be his idea, fully internalized, but the direction and the suggestion will initially have come from the treating team.

Where the young patient is not given such support and such direction as he moves back into the community, he is liable to find himself befriended only by the lonely and by the deviant in society. Since the adolescent peer groupings are already established and difficult to break into, the adolescent patient is liable to attract only the solitary, the inadequate and the delinquent teenagers who themselves have been unable to succeed socially and emotionally. Indeed, caring personnel found it almost routinely correct that the first steady acquaintances made by the adolescent patient as he enters the public school setting are teenagers usually as disturbed as, or frequently more disturbed emotionally than, the patient himself. Hopefully, as the adolescent continues to mature and to grow emotionally, he will seek more gratifying relationships elsewhere. The treatment team must constantly beware lest unhealthy relationships in the community slow down or prevent further emotional growth in the teenage patient.

LEAVING THE ADOLESCENT UNIT

In time, after the expenditure of much pain and energy, the adolescent is emotionally ready to move from the more protected residential environment. His behavior has changed to the point where he can handle his inner tensions through his own strengths, complemented at times by normal environmental supports. He uses most of his emotional and intellectual energy toward personal growth and productivity and he gains gratification and increasing strength from such ego mastery. He has a moderately accurate concept of his own capabilities and his own limitations as well as some ideas of his goal in life. Usually the residential team members have a great deal of ambivalence about allowing the adolescent to move finally into the wider social community.

It may be difficult for therapeutic staff members to see the departure of adolescent patients as the maximum reward they receive from months and years of hard work and personal investment in the young man or woman. "They just get to be fun to be around and then they go." "You really get to like them when suddenly they go."

Frequently it is difficult for caring personnel to allow the adolescent to move from the hospital setting into the community in an emotional state less exalted than sainthood. Often the treatment team appear to require perfection from the

89

patient as an indication that he is ready to leave. The treatment staff hesitate to let the teenager venture forth and to make mistakes lest he be hurt—but of course he will be hurt and it is with their training and their strengthening that he should now be able to stand that hurt. If the teenager is bad or if he tells lies occasionally, the treatment personnel wonder whether he is ready to move from the hospital environment; somehow the staff tend to forget that most people occasionally lie or are wicked and have to take the full responsibility for their misdeeds, as the adolescent patient must also do when he moves into society. If emotionally he is really ready to make such a growth move, he should also be able to face the social expectation for truth and to bear the punishment for any lies.

The adolescent patient and the treatment team go through a period of mourning before and after the departure of the adolescent from the hospital setting so that the treatment program can be as meaningful as possible and finally integrated both for the adolescent and for the staff members. If there has been a meaningful interaction of any kind, positive or negative, this separation will necessitate an emotional readjustment in all involved. The teenage patient may insist that he has hated everyone consistently. If this proclamation is true, and it is rarely completely true, this adolescent has obviously had a most meaningful relationship, albeit based on hatred. For this teenager to leave the hospital setting with a necessarily complete emotional separation and to be able to grow in the community away from the hospital, he needs to face this meaning of final separation from those he says he hates and, in his own way, go through as much of a mourning process as a teenager who openly admits that he is leaving people for whom he genuinely cares (Easson, 1967c). The treatment team and the teenage patient must face the sadness, the loneliness and the anger over this necessary final separation. The sadness at losing a meaningful relationship is easy to recognize, to face, and to handle. Separation anger is more difficult to tolerate. Both the therapeutic team and the adolescent patient think it is unreasonable to feel angry or irritated that the latter is moving away—everyone should be happy because he is leaving and making progress or everyone should be relieved to see the last of this pest. In reality the teenager and the treatment team are losing a meaningful relationship and the loss hurts even though logically they are happy or relieved. In their hurt and in the hurt felt by the leaving adolescent, both the teenage patient and staff members tend to react angrily toward each other. Many adolescent patients openly state it is "easier to leave angry." The staff anger and irritation at these times of separation may be focused on the imperfections that can be found in every departing patient or in the inadequacies that can be discovered in any member of the treatment team.

As the teenage patient moves from the hospital setting, he gives up the emotional support of the hospital (Safirstein, 1967). Temporarily his ego strength is weakened by this loss of external support and will stay weaker until gradually he can build up his emotional strength and capability to compensate for this ego loss. In the anxiety of the separation from the hospital setting, the departing adolescent has less personal emotional capacity to deal with this increase in inner tension. It is at this time of separation that the treatment team tend to see some recapitulation of the original illness. Old symptoms tend to recur in mild or comparatively transient forms. Previous sick patterns of coping with tension appear once more in the teenager. Such a recrudescence of former symptoms may further accentuate the doubts of the adolescent and the staff about his leaving. If indeed the teenager is ready to leave the residential setting, this echo of old sick behavioral patterns should be less pronounced than the original illness, more easily controlled and comparatively short lived. Under these circumstances, the adolescent should be helped to continue his emotional separation from the hospital environment and should be supported to form stronger ties outside the hospital setting. He should be given greater encouragement to increase his emotional investment in outside peer activity, in his new home and in his long-term plan, for these outside emotional ties and supports will partially compensate for the loss of hospital support. The main emotional compensation for the loss of residential direction will come from the teenager's continued ego growth. The treatment team must be very much aware of and even anticipate this symptomatic recrudescence at the time of separation from the hospital lest in the anger and the ambivalence around the leaving process, such a symptomatic exacerbation is used as a reason to delay a necessary process in the teenager's treatment growth. Some disturbed adolescents will never reach the level of emotional capability where they can function totally outside a hospital setting or without continued environmental support. For such adolescents it may be necessary to allow them to separate only partially from the hospital environment and to continue to maintain as many hospital ties and as much hospital support as they require.

When the adolescent patient is emotionally ready to leave the inpatient setting he should leave. The treatment staff must transfer their therapeutic energy from the departing patient to those patients who are left and are ready to come. As in any meaningful mourning process, the mourners gain maximum solace in turning to a new future, to other patients, and to other challenges. If the separation and the mourning process is not dealt with constructively, persistent anger and anxiety is liable to be expressed toward the patient who is leaving, toward other patients, or toward fellow staff members. The caring team must learn early in their professional experience that their greatest personal reward with any adolescent patient comes with the final handshake and firm march to the open door, away from them.

Chapter V

The Prescription of Psychotherapy for the Disturbed Adolescent

This 16 year old boy should be admitted to the inpatient unit so that he can receive meaningful psychotherapy.

With such a referral, disturbed adolescents not infrequently are sent for examination under the therapeutic misapprehension that a need for psychotherapy is a valid reason for hospital admission. No troubled adolescent should be admitted to an inpatient setting specifically to receive only psychotherapy. If psychotherapy is the total treatment program the teenager requires, individual or group psychotherapy can be better provided on an outpatient basis. If the adolescent is so lacking in personal emotional strength and in the capability to use meaningful environmental relationship supports, these emotional handicaps should be considered openly with the adolescent and with his family; inpatient hospital treatment should then be recommended because this is the specific treatment modality the adolescent requires. In such an instance, hospital treatment is the recommended therapeutic prescription to which psychotherapy may be added if this seems appropriate. A clear, meaningful examination and an explicit treatment prescription helps the disturbed adolescent and his family to progress through a necessary growth stage in the long-term treatment process. The adolescent and his family must meaningfully face the reason and the purpose for the prescription of residential therapy so that they can usefully integrate the total therapeutic process.

If psychotherapy is considered to be necessary and beneficial in addition to the intensive milieu treatment process provided in the inpatient unit, psychotherapy can then be prescribed and tailored to the individual needs of the adolescent patient. Many teenage inpatients have already been through a succession of outpatient psychotherapy processes. Many adolescents have been evaluated, examined, and tested by a succession of psychologists, psychiatrists, and social workers. A large percentage of these disturbed teenagers have started in a psychotherapy process, been involved to some extent, and then ended the psychotherapy relationship with various degrees of emotional trauma. Often these disturbed adolescents come to the inpatient setting well versed in the jargon of psychotherapy. They use words such as "defense," "projection," "rationalization" and "anxiety" easily and aggressively. Frequently this language of former psychotherapy processes is used as an emotional barrier against any new meaningful treatment process. For many disturbed adolescents, an intensive milieu therapy program provides the total therapeutic approach that they require and are able to use.

In an inpatient setting, psychotherapy should never be prescribed for all adolescent patients in an encompassing fashion whereby every teenager is routinely given a psychotherapist. Psychotherapy is a potent, specific therapeutic instrument and, as such, needs to be carefully prescribed with an understanding of the patient's needs and capabilities. If the guiding theories of a treatment setting demand that all patients be placed in an individual psychotherapy process, one specific admission criterion for that treatment unit must be that all the patients admitted should have sufficient personality strength and relationship capability to use a psychotherapy process. For some disturbed adolescents, psychotherapy may not bring emotional benefit but rather may cause personality handicapping, regression and disruption. For individual adolescent patients, for clearly understood, well defined therapeutic reasons, it may be considered beneficial and growth promoting to prescribe for these patients a course of individual or group psychotherapy. Before this psychotherapy prescription is made, several criteria should be met.

1. A psychotherapy process must be based on the adolescent patient's individual emotional potential and on his capacity to form meaningful relationships. Because such relationships can be meaningful to this teenage patient, psychotherapy—relationship therapy—may be prescribed to move and to support this patient in a growth-producing direction.

2. The psychotherapy process, like any other meaningful treatment process with the disturbed adolescent, must mobilize sufficient personal anxiety and emotional energy to promote behavioral change and growth.

3. The adolescent patient must be able to cope with and use this anxiety aroused in the psychotherapy process, together with the controls and strengths available to him, either in the form of his own inner emotional strengths or the external ego structuring provided him in the inpatient setting.

To some more troubled adolescents, the emotional closeness of any meaningful relationship brings to consciousness unbearable feelings—the deepest most overwhelming loneliness, the nightmarish loss of personal boundaries and of individual integrity and the surge of explosive, engulfing, destructive angers and impulses. Such adolescents require emotional distance which allows them to maintain their integrity. Some of these very fragile, uncertain adolescents can verbalize the threat implied by a close relationship whereas other teenagers can only act out their spiraling anxiety in face of such a relationship, and the least adequate teenagers can only regress further emotionally in face of an intolerable closeness. Because certain adolescent inpatients do lack the necessary personality strength or are unable to use external ego supports, the treatment team cannot ask these disturbed adolescents to assume the anxiety and the burden of a direct psychotherapy relationship at that time. For an extended period of months or years, or perhaps even for the duration of the total treatment process, these teenagers may be better helped by the more distant relationship treatment provided by the hospital environmental therapy and by peer group interactions.

In a tenuous and uncertain fashion, some disturbed adolescents may be able to maintain and to use a meaningful individual psychotherapy treatment relationship; as a specifically prescribed treatment measure, a psychotherapy process may be prescribed for these teenagers to enhance gently but firmly their very limited relationship capability. An individual psychotherapy process offers such a patient the security and the structured limits of an interaction with only one person where the relationship opportunities are strictly contained by the time limits of the therapy appointment. In an individual psychotherapy session, no matter how open and how direct the patient may be about expressing his feelings, the end of the appointment session at least partially brings a limit and a control to this emotional expression. A strictly enforced time schedule for the therapeutic interview gives such patients the added certainty of external controls which further reinforce the boundaries within which their emotional feelings and impulses are contained. These teenagers know that, even if their feelings do slip beyond their control, at the end of an appointment hour, definite time controls are provided. If these adolescent patients allow themselves to share feelings freely in the residential setting, their day-to-day environment normally does not provide such discrete definite time boundaries. Once these uncertain adolescents begin to express feelings within the residential unit, they may find themselves in a frightening predicament in which they cannot stop or control this emotional flooding and where environmental controls are ambiguous. If their personal dilemma is not appreciated and if they cannot withdraw, a mounting flood of anxiety-arousing feelings may lead to emotional disruption and regression. For the more disturbed teenager, the initial experience of expressing and of sharing feelings must be established in a very controlled, supported situation. Psychotherapy thus may be prescribed to allow these adolescents to try to share and express themselves very tentatively with one specific person in a very structured, definite, time limited life situation. Since these fragile immature adolescents are so uncertain and distrustful, it is essential initially that psychotherapy appointments are kept firmly fixed and stable if a meaningful relationship is to be maintained.

Where an adolescent can relate to other human beings only as to part objects or in a preambivalent fashion (see Chapter VIII), a psychotherapy treatment process may be prescribed to help him develop this very limited relationship ability. When the adolescent patient relates at such a primitive object level, it is fairly certain that a meaningful individual psychotherapeutic process will temporarily cause him to withdraw emotionally from the residential setting. With his very limited relationship capacity, his emotional interaction and sharing may be contained almost totally within the therapeutic process; only when he grows emotionally in strength and personal integration will his ability to relate extend gradually outside the psychotherapy interview. Where it is diagnostically clear that the disturbed adolescent has the emotional capability to relate to only one or two people in this limited fashion, it is essential that the total treatment team support with understanding the individual psychotherapy process through such a period of comparative emotional unavailability within the residential unit. With such an emotionally limited adolescent, there is a treatment danger that he may grow emotionally only within the context of the therapeutic relationship. The psychotherapist must be on his guard lest he perpetuate such an emotional split in the treatment and such a stunting in his patient. With some adolescent patients, basic emotional resources may be so limited that the total treatment goal will be to help them maintain one meaningful relationship; in the therapeutic situation with such a limited teenager, the treatment team must support him to exist comfortably within the framework of his limited relationship capability. Quite deliberately individual psychotherapy may be prescribed for such a teenager to enhance even this most limited capacity for interaction.

Many authors who write about the psychotherapeutic process with the disturbed adolescent suggest that any successful psychotherapist has to be a special kind of person (Greaves and Regan, 1957; Hendrickson, Holmes, and Waggoner, 1959). In reality the treatment process with the adolescent is indeed characteristically intense, at times searingly active, at other times deadeningly torpid. In this treatment process, the adolescent shows wide surges of emotional and physical energy and the most primitive, pungent, direct forms of communication. The therapeutic process is not totally unpredictable as has been suggested, but rather is relatively fluid and responsive to the teenager's inner directed and externally provoked stimuli. Most directly and usually most honestly, the adolescent will express feelings of love, hate, sexuality, and need. Not only does the adolescent communicate his own feelings extensively on a nonverbal level, but he also responds maximally to the preverbal communication of the psychotherapist (Lewin, 1965). Intuitively and very directly, the teenage patient spontaneously reads his psychotherapist—the therapist's appearance, dress and posture, his office and his general manner. The psychotherapist for the disturbed adolescent cannot be artificial as the teenager, through his understanding of the many nonverbal cues provided by the psychotherapist, will quickly see through a façade and will very likely expose mercilessly this deception (a deception which is often the psychotherapist's own self-deception). In every form of psychotherapy relationship, the therapist must be comfortable with his own self-image so that the adolescent has someone secure and definite with whom to relate and to react.

Optimally, the adolescent and the psychotherapist should share a strong empathic bond. Much of the adolescent patient's relationship ability is narcissistically based and directed. He likes people who understand him, who talk his language and who are "for him." Without a firm basis of mutual empathy, a psychotherapy process is difficult to begin and almost impossible to maintain with the disturbed adolescent. During periods of high anxiety and disruptive conflicts in the psychotherapy process, often it is only the strong mutual empathic tie between the teenager and the psychotherapist that maintains the necessary continuity of the treatment process. The adolescent patient must be sure that his psychotherapist is "on his side," no matter how disturbing the psychotherapeutic interpretations may be. On many occasions it is the adolescent's conflict between his inner certainty that his psychotherapist has his special interest at heart and "knows" him and the reality that this relationship process is arousing disturbing feelings that first produces behavioral change.

> [As an 18 year old young man said]: I didn't like what you were saying, but you and I usually see things the same way. I figured you must make sense somewhere so I looked and looked and, darn it, you did make sense—and I wish you had not.

When a psychotherapeutic relationship that has been founded on this empathic-narcissistic basis, grows to a meaningful alliance between two separate human beings, the strength of this treatment bond will survive and flourish through the recurrent anxieties of the treatment process. If the therapeutic relationship does not grow but remains at a purely narcissistic, empathically based level, the adolescent patient can easily transfer the focus of his narcissism elsewhere. If the treatment is maintained only at this narcissistic level, the adolescent patient has the experience of relating only to the psychotherapist as a focus for his own narcissism. The adolescent does not have the necessary growth experience that comes from relating with another human being whom he perceives as even slightly different from himself. Though an empathic tie is essential early in the psychotherapy process with the adolescent, the treatment interaction should develop beyond this narcissistically oriented level if the psychotherapy relationship is to be of long-term treatment value.

99

The psychotherapist should be particularly careful not to arouse strong or conflictual feelings based and focused upon himself, too early in the treatment process (Holmes, 1964, p. 221; Beckett, 1965, p. 76). For a severely disturbed adolescent girl it would be most difficult to maintain a continued psychotherapeutic process with a young male psychotherapist—not because such a therapeutic relationship might not be beneficial and growth producing in the long-run, but rather because early in this treatment process the young girl naturally experiences strong and disturbing sexual feelings toward the therapist. Although the male psychotherapist naturally arouses disturbing tensions, he cannot have a totally empathic understanding of these strong erotic feelings. In a similar fashion, an impulse ridden teenage boy would find it impossible to maintain a psychotherapeutic relationship with a young woman therapist.

> Everytime I looked at her, I wanted to screw her. She has the best set of boobs this side of Chicago. That's not fair to a guy who has not had a piece of ass since Christmas. We just couldn't go on.

In this treatment situation, the woman psychotherapist realistically cannot have the necessary empathic understanding of this young man's sexual feelings so that patient and therapist can sustain this most difficult beginning stage of the psychotherapy process. In such a treatment relationship, a female psychotherapist would arouse disruptive anxiety in any action oriented adolescent if she tried to focus on these feelings or on the teenager's method of coping with these tensions. At all levels of treatment with disturbed adolescents similar reality-based treatment difficulties occur. It may be impossible to maintain young attractive women aides or housekeeping personnel on a unit for disturbed teenage boys; these young patients lack the necessary ego strength to control the anxieties and the impulses aroused by the mere presence of these treatment personnel. Disturbed adolescent girls cannot tolerate emotionally the presence of male college students as permanent inpatient team members.

The adolescents who are admitted to the hospital setting feel they have been repeatedly rejected and betrayed during their short lives. It is necessary for them constantly to test the strengths and the stability of each member of the treatment team. During the psychotherapeutic process, the teenage patient will test repeatedly to see if the psychotherapist is a person of strength and integrity. For the adolescent to use the psychotherapist meaningfully in his own growth and identification processes, it is essential that the teenager become absolutely sure that the psychotherapist respects himself and is a person worthy of respect. In an adolescent residential unit where smoking is forbidden, it is a routine early testing maneuver in the psychotherapy process for the adolescent patient to ask the psychotherapist casually, ever so casually, for matches to smoke contraband cigarettes during the session. If the unsuspecting, kindly psychotherapist provides these matches—a natural social gesture—he is instantly labeled as friendly but weak, as easily seduced to break the established rules of the residential setting and thus in the long-run as not trustworthy. The adolescent patient feels, with much justification, that if the psychotherapist is so easily undermined and seduced in the psychotherapy setting, he can be just as easily enticed to betray the adolescent patient elsewhere. Sometimes this seductive aggressiveness toward the psychotherapist is even more open and more challenging. The adolescent may bring alcohol or drugs into the psychotherapy interviews to test the strength and the self-respect of the psychotherapist. These angry disrespectful gestures must be faced directly and discussed openly within the therapeutic relationship. The adolescent may be struggling with his conflictual need to destroy an increasingly significant emotional tie with his psychotherapist because he fears that this bond will strangle his independence or will force him into an unmanly, dependent relationship. If the adolescent patient is unable or unwilling to respect the psychotherapist and the psychotherapy process, it may be most therapeutic for the psychotherapist to terminate the psychotherapy interviews either temporarily or permanently, if the adolescent continues to abuse the privileges of such a potentially meaningful relationship. The psychotherapist must indicate to the adolescent that he respects both himself and the adolescent so much that he will not tolerate the latter's wasting their time. If the psychotherapist continues a treatment relationship where he feels he is being constantly derided, abused, and disrespected, he will himself be undermining the treatment process. He is allowing the psychotherapy relationship to be used merely as an avenue for unproductive behavior. For many teenage patients, the most meaningful experience in the treatment process has been the psychotherapist's insistence on due, reasonable respect for himself and the treatment process. Noshpitz (1957) details how the psychotherapist must indeed prove and maintain his self-respect and his realistically based standards.

Many of these disturbed adolescents have had parents who did not seek and who were not worthy of the respect of their children; since these parents were not respected by their children, they were thus not available as meaningful identification figures. The psychotherapist must give the adolescent a different and more enriching treatment experience. The psychotherapist has to demonstrate to the adolescent patient that he is a warm, definite, reality based, self-respecting person whose sole task is to help the teenager gain the maximum emotional benefit and greatest personal growth from whatever the teenager does in his psychotherapy sessions and in his daily living. When this principle of mutual self-respect and treatment strength is established, the psychotherapist is then free to discuss with the teenage patient both sides of any question—the breaking and the maintaining of the "no smoking" rule, the pleasures and the pains of sexual gratification, the rewards and the penalties of "goofing off," the joys of dependency, and the frustrations of independence. In the psychotherapy process, the adolescent patient will need to prove over and over again that the psychotherapist is not invested for his own emotional gratification but solely to bring the maximum benefit to the teenager. The adolescent will have to become absolutely convinced that the psychotherapist is striving primarily to help him utilize his own capabilities and potentialities. The young patient will test repeatedly to make sure that the psychotherapist does not regard him as a source of gratification, in a manner similar to the adolescent's parents who viewed their child merely as a narcissistic extension.

In the usual course of treatment, the psychotherapist himself does not take the private discussion material outside the treatment sessions because the adolescent must be constantly certain of the confidentiality of his treatment process (Malmquist, 1965). In dealing with the most uncertain, most paranoid teenage patients, the psychotherapist may find it necessary to say practically nothing of the treatment process to other treatment team members. In the beginning stage of treatment, the paranoid adolescent does not have sufficient ego strength and trusting ability to tolerate any discussion of psychotherapy outside of the treatment sessions without rupture of the psychotherapeutic relationship. As the treatment bond becomes stronger, it is possible and essential for the psychotherapist to share his treatment understanding with other members of the team.

It is totally unnecessary for the psychotherapist to reveal any specific private details of the psychotherapy sessions. Too frequently poorly digested, misunderstood information merely causes tension within the treatment team without leading to better management. When the adolescent patient and the treatment team trust the psychotherapist to share meaningfully an understanding of the treatment process, the adolescent patient begins to live an experience of mutual trust. He learns to depend on the decision of someone outside himself as the understanding of his feelings and conflicts are shared by his psychotherapist with the total treatment team. The psychotherapist must constantly emphasize to the adolescent that the final decisions belong to the patient himself. Outside of the psychotherapy sessions, the adolescent has the awesome responsibility

103

of deciding and taking full responsibility, although the psychotherapist will help the teenager as much as possible within the
psychotherapy sessions.

One definite rule pervades the entire treatment process—the
psychotherapist must maintain the constant reality that he will
not allow the adolescent to hurt himself permanently or to
hurt other people. This treatment principle frequently becomes a crucial focus of psychotherapy when the teenage patient tests the psychotherapist to see whether the latter does
indeed hold the teenager's safety and security as being of vital
importance. If, in the interest of rigid, inflexible confidentiality, the psychotherapist keeps totally private the reality that
this adolescent is about to inflict some kind of permanent dam-
age, the adolescent has then seduced the psychotherapist into
maintaining this psychotherapeutic confidentiality solely for
the latter's own narcissistic gratification. If it does appear that
someone is about to be hurt severely, the psychotherapist
should tell the patient as far in advance as possible that, for his
own protection as well as that of other people, he is considering
breaking the confidentiality of psychotherapy. The therapist
must take pains to fully explain to the teenager why he is
making this decision. While the total confidentiality of the
treatment process is vitally important, even more important is
the adolescent patient's certainty that the psychotherapist will
do nothing and will allow nothing that may permanently harm
the teenager. The psychotherapist must be strong enough to
prevent the teenager from hurting himself, because the therapist has the adolescent patient's interest at stake. The decision
of the psychotherapist to act to prevent the teenage patient
from hurting himself may lead to a crucial psychotherapeutic
interaction that may build the strongest relationship bond
which can survive any later anxiety. In such a fashion, the
teenager will have tested and will have found for himself that,
above all else, the psychotherapist had the teenager's interest
at heart—even at the risk of disrupting a mutually gratifying
therapeutic relationship. This awareness of the psychothera-

pist's altruistic investment in their growth and achievement may prove so threatening for some uncertain adolescents that they may have to bring the treatment process to an end. The psychotherapist can rest assured that if he has maintained his self-respect, his respect for the adolescent, and the respect for the strength of the treatment relationship, and if he has shown the adolescent that it is truly possible to gain gratification from the growth of others, the psychotherapeutic relationship will remain with the adolescent as a source of continued strength and as an example of how much personal interaction he is able to successfully integrate.

The psychotherapy prescription can be increased or decreased, changed or adjusted depending on the needs of the individual adolescent patient. At some point in the treatment process, the treatment team may consider it necessary and appropriate to alter the frequency of the psychotherapy session. With an appreciation of the emotional growth and changes of the adolescent patient, the teenager may be shifted from group psychotherapy to individual psychotherapy or vice versa, or one psychotherapy process may be added to the other. All treatment changes should be integrated with the teenager's growth process. The psychotic adolescent may use a supportive individual psychotherapy process early in his treatment situation to help him better adjust to his peer group; once this teenager has moved successfully into his age appropriate group, he may be better supported in the milieu treatment process provided by the residential unit. For the maturing psychotic adolescent, his individual psychotherapy process may then have become a situation which invited regression or tolerated emotional withdrawal behind closed doors. As a necessary growth stage this individual process should then be meaningfully terminated and group psychotherapy started if this treatment move seemed appropriate.

Where the adolescent makes a special use of the empathic patient-therapist bond, it might be therapeutically beneficial to change the psychotherapist during the course of the treatment process. Initially the disturbed adolescent may have to express his inner tensions and energies in action directed fashions and may respond most empathically to an action oriented therapist. As this teenager grows emotionally and moves toward more sublimated, less activity-oriented defenses, it may then be helpful to change him as part of a meaningful, ongoing treatment process to another psychotherapist who is more empathic with less action-prone patterns of behavior. The first psychotherapy relationship can be terminated and the reasons for this termination realistically faced and worked through, both by the adolescent patient and his psychotherapist, to allow for the fullest and best integrated internalization of this initial relationship. The second psychotherapy treatment relationship can then be assumed in a situation where the new therapist and the adolescent deal openly with the reasons for this treatment shift. The immature adolescent may respond very well to the empathic warmth of a motherly woman psychotherapist so that gradually he learns in the treatment relationship to relate ambivalently to human beings; when he matures emotionally to the point where he can deal with more direct sexual feelings and where he must begin to form definite masculine identifications, it may then be better to transfer him to a comfortable male therapist where mutual masculinity can heighten and can strengthen the treatment process. Stierlin (1961), in his discussion of the psychotherapy process of the hospitalized psychotic patient, emphasizes this "nonexploiting solidarity" that the patient must have with his psychotherapist.

Treatment occurs only by consent of the patient. Many teenagers will never acknowledge that they are "sick" or that they really need any form of treatment. The very fact that they do maintain themselves in a treatment process, either in the residential unit or in the psychotherapy situation, is sufficient outward personal indication of treatment investment. A more overt proclamation of commitment would be seen by most adolescents as being too infantile, too degrading and too dependent. For the psychotherapist to demand an open declaration of "sickness" would be considered by the teenage patient as an action solely to gratify the psychotherapist.

Many adolescents will make excellent use of peer support to work through the anxieties and the conflicts of their individual psychotherapy. Frequently the young patient will go directly from his individual psychotherapy session and, in a most productive fashion, will discuss with his peers the material of his private hours. In a huddle over the dining room table, he will relate with raucous laughter some details of his discussion with his psychotherapist—and so handle his anxiety over this material in a growth-promoting fashion. With other patients of the psychotherapist he will compare in detail how the therapist acted and what he said. These teenage patients will note and laugh together at the repetition and the consistency in their separate psychotherapy hours but they will find relief in the fact that the psychotherapist is constant even when they themselves are not present. Some psychotherapists try to forbid such discussions outside the psychotherapy sessions (Holmes, 1964, p. 93). Such prohibition is impossible to enforce and is also totally nontherapeutic. A comfortable, meaningful psychotherapy process is maintained and indeed is enhanced by these extratherapy discussions. Most disturbed adolescents do not have the emotional capability to contain their anxiety totally within the enforced limitations of the psychotherapy hours. The secure psychotherapist can greatly enrich the treatment regimen by discussing these extra-therapeutic processes within the actual therapy sessions.

Where the adolescent does not have the necessary emotional ability or the personal need for individual psychotherapy but where he shows an ability to relate to his peers, a group psychotherapy program may be usefully prescribed. In this fashion his relationship capability can be encouraged, supported, and promoted within this wider peer group interaction. Where an individual psychotherapy process may be felt by the teenager to be too unstructured and too threateningly close, the disturbed adolescent may be able to use the external personality supports and the growth opportunities provided by an activity or a shared purpose group, such as a unit council meeting, to help him react meaningfully with group members (Cameron, 1953). A productive treatment group may be established around a common interest in athletics, in auto mechanics, or in woodworking. Teenage girls may learn to interact in a group cosmetics activity, in a movie outing group, or in shared cooking sessions. A therapeutic group may be formed by focusing on a common group problem such as the first move into a public school setting or the initial teenage attempts at heterosexual social relationships. In these group oriented programs, the treatment team members can show as much reasonable warmth and personal empathy as the adolescent group members can tolerate and use.

The Quality of the Psychotherapy Process

I have never met anyone who can ignore me so actively. Her absolute disinterest in me is so direct and so intense that it fills the room.

Any psychotherapist who has dealt with adolescent patients can remember such a feeling in the psychotherapy situation. In the treatment relationship with the adolescent, the therapeutic interaction at every level is characteristically most intense. This treatment intensity comes from the high level of energy available to the adolescent, the marked sensitivity and intuitiveness of most teenagers, and the very direct, comparatively uninhibited, all-encompassing approach of most adolescents.

Everything the adolescent is, does, and says is a direct resonant communication to which the psychotherapist can be expected to respond in some fashion. The young lady waddles into the office, spreadeagles herself across the chair, and blows her nose loudly—her sloppiness, her awkwardness, and her emotional heaviness have begun a very direct, very personal communication to the psychotherapist. The young man whistles nonchalantly past the therapist, waves at a friend through the office window, very, very casually lights his cigarette, and yawns—already a very intense communication process has been established in the treatment setting. The sensitive psychotherapist of the adolescent patient must train himself or herself to gauge the emotional status of the teenage patient by the heaviness and the speed of the footfall approaching the door, the length of the stop at the water cooler, and the profundity of the sigh after drinking—before the adolescent patient actually appears physically in the office doorway. This therapeutic attention and sensitivity to the teenager's feelings and self-expression early in each psychotherapy session is not merely an intellectual luxury but rather a treatment necessity; the adolescent patient does not give the psychotherapist any extended period of introductory time to gauge the young patient's emotional status but rather the treatment interaction is an active process immediately when the patient and the psychotherapist come into contact.

Hi Willie, had a good weekend?

As the 16 year old young man bounces jauntily into the psychotherapy office, he greets his male therapist in this warm, familiar but challenging fashion. The psychotherapist is aware that this teenage patient does in fact feel very warmly toward him; indeed, the adolescent has expressed the direct wish that the therapist in some way should be his father. Any discussion about the psychotherapist's weekend activities is thus weighted heavily by the teenager's wish for closeness and need for emotional distance, for understanding, and emancipation. Though the patient is a physically active young man, his stride into the office is too bouncy and jerky. His hair is long and straggly; today it hangs over his face. As he puffs strenuously on his cigarette, the teenager looks strangely young; this youthful appearance is accentuated by his cutoff jeans and his bright sleeveless, yellow T-shirt. The psychotherapist knows that any conscious awareness of his regressive or childlike feelings would cause this proud sensitive fragile young man to withdraw emotionally. The promise of direct, open warmth will cause this teenager so much anxiety that he can only protect himself through an angry attacking outburst. On the few occasions when this young man can allow himself to be openly warm and caring, he tends to become very much younger in his physical appearance; his face loses the lines of care and tension and appears like that of a very young child.

Thus the therapist responds, "Not too good. I just couldn't sleep for worrying that, with your bare knees, you would catch pneumonia." Especially when considered out of context, this is a bizarre response, although the quality of reply does have a definite purpose. In any continued psychotherapy process with a teenage patient, the psychotherapist and the adolescent develop their own mutually understood language. In their shared language, the psychotherapist here has again affirmed his warm, continued interest in the young man; the therapist has however transferred the focus of the discussion back to the teenager and, in a barely concealed metaphor, has indicated his understanding from the patient's appearance that the young man is experiencing a regressive pull. The concerned warmth and the empathic, though joking, answer sets the tone for a discussion of warm feelings which the adolescent can tolerate. The psychotherapist has deliberately set a pattern for the hour which would be difficult to break. This discussion, progressing from the reality of bare knees and cutoff jeans to the actuality of the past weekend, quickly highlights how profoundly lonely the young man was over the weekend. The psychotherapist and the teenager again consider together his wish for a warm, close, understanding relationship, the kind of closeness which he knows intellectually that he can no longer obtain from his parents because he is too old, and emotionally they and he are too distant from each other. Thus it is within the treatment process that this young man must face these unsatisfied needs and longings and must mourn his hopeless yearnings. When he has worked through the mourning process, he should be well on his way to emotional independence and stability.

This simple vignette highlights many factors in the group and in the individual psychotherapy processes with every teenage patient. At all times, between the psychotherapist and the teenage patient there must be a sincere strong bond of respect. The psychotherapist must always respect the adolescent as a young man or a young woman of integrity. If the therapist does not have this strong personal respect for the teenager, it is very dubious whether he will be able to maintain any satisfactory treatment process on behalf of his teenage patient. This sincere meaningful respect on the part of the psychotherapist is a constant goad for the young patient's emotional growth, a goad for which the teenager is both proud and periodically infuriated.

Damnation, I wish you wouldn't believe in me so darn much. You take away half the fun of goofing off!

Where there is this mutual respect, communication between the teenage patient and the psychotherapist is usually easy and direct though at times such interaction may be fraught with anxiety and pain. Sometimes it is stated that the psychotherapist must talk the slang of the teenager. The language of the adolescent is direct pungent English, highlighted by a multiplicity of nonverbal cues. It is essential for the therapist to understand the adolescent slang but the self-respecting therapist talks naturally, directly, and honestly in his own individual manner. The psychotherapist must be aware how many adolescents use words and phrases that are common in general society and in adult culture but with a specific teenage meaning and significance. The psychotherapist himself does not need to talk in adolescent jargon for he has to respect and to value his own self-style.

The teenager's psychotherapist quickly learns to communicate on many emotional levels at the same time and to shift rapidly between these levels. The psychotherapist notes how the young man can discuss in detail his latest sexual conquests while, without thinking, he sucks his thumb. The teenage girl will talk ferociously about her plans to claw out her roommate's eyes while, like a little child, she twirls her hair. During periods of tension, the self-sufficient young man will eat his way through a whole dish of candy. As she mourns the loss of her latest boyfriend, the young adolescent girl will nurse and tenderly caress her cigarette. Most often these cues are not interpreted directly or are discussed only in metaphor during the treatment process. These communications are accepted at the unconscious, nonverbal level at which they are given and are only interpreted by the psychotherapist if he feels that such interpretation would benefit the adolescent. In the active treatment metaphor, the psychotherapist may plan in detail over a period of several months with a young adolescent man a program of weight building to build up his muscles; they may never discuss directly the ego strengthening process which is being built up in the therapeutic relationship. With an uncertain 17 year old boy, the psychotherapist may spend many months in considering with him how he might take over his father's business and run it more effectively. In such a very obvious therapy meta-phor and in the continued relationship with the psychothera-pist, this young man is working toward a more useful resolution of his conflictual feelings with his own father; frequently such treatment work is maintained totally within the therapeutic metaphor.

Quite often the psychotherapy process is maintained at a totally nonverbal and totally empathic level of interaction. Thus a psychotherapist may write the following note:

> John was waiting for me when I arrived today. His hair was tousled and awry. He wore a crumpled white sweatshirt and his tattered, faded cutoff jeans. His shoes were unkempt and without polish. Wordlessly he followed me to the office, slumped in his favorite rocking chair and sat with his head in his hands. His face was gray, drawn, tired, and haggard. We sat silently for the whole hour. He never looked directly toward me but quickly there seemed to build up between us a shared sense of profound mourning. The whole room seemed filled with an intense sharing process. To me (the therapist), this was a very moving hour at the end of which I felt completely drained.

Were the psychotherapist to try to put into words the feelings shared in these hours, such an attempt would appear artificial and stupid to the teenager; the adolescent patient would react with realistic anger because the psychotherapist would be trying to establish a communication where already a very meaningful communication existed.

THE PRESCRIPTION OF PSYCHOTHERAPY

All psychotherapy specifically prescribed for an individual adolescent is supportive and interpretive in differing degrees, whether the psychotherapy process is group or individually oriented. These supportive and interpretive functions of the psychotherapy process can be accentuated and varied depend-ing on the needs of the individual teenager. An interpretive psychotherapy process is directed toward uncovering and under-standing maladaptive defenses so that these inefficient coping mechanisms can be discarded and the energy, freed up, used toward more efficient patterns of behavior and toward emotional growth. Supportive psychotherapy is planned toward enhancing and strengthening existing defenses and behavior patterns; although defense mechanisms that limit or handicap emotional growth can be modified and adapted, they are usually not replaced by more positive mechanisms in a psychotherapy process that is purely supportive. In an interpretive psychotherapy treatment program, as the patient's inefficient and maladaptive ego defenses are examined and discarded, the teenage patient temporarily goes through a period when his total ego defenses are considerably reduced. In this transition stage, as emotionally unproductive defenses are given up and before new defenses have been developed, there is a temporary weakening in the patient's total ego capability to cope with anxiety. To make full use of an interpretive psychotherapy process, the disturbed adolescent must have sufficient inner ego strength and adequate external emotional supports to tolerate without disruptive anxiety this temporary removal of even these relatively inefficient ego supports. Since residential treatment is prescribed only for adolescent patients who do require definite external ego strengthening and structure, by definition, these patients on admission lack the necessary personality strength for a classical uncovering analytic psychotherapy process. On the successful completion of their residential treatment program, these young patients may then have sufficient ego strength to enter a full analytic process should this prescription be considered therapeutically appropriate; at the time of their hospitalization, an uncovering interpretive psychotherapy program would cause such patients more emotional stress than their fragile ego capabilities could tolerate.

In this psychotherapy process with the disturbed adolescent, interpretations can and should be made at different emotional levels at different times, using the same therapy material. It is not necessary at any specific time in the psychotherapy interaction to work through an anxiety-arousing conflict at all emotional levels; rather, it is possible and preferable to refer back in the treatment process to previous discussions. This harkeningback not only allows specific conflict to be considered further when the adolescent can tolerate such deeper discussions but, in maintaining a treatment process integrated across time, the adolescent is helped to integrate and to internalize meaningful ongoing relationships and experiences.

In a psychotherapy discussion with a 15 year old young man about an episode where he had sexual relationships with his girlfriend in her living room, it was possible to consider immediately with him the markedly exhibitionistic quality of his behavior. At a later time, several months after the event, the psychotherapist discussed with the teenage patient the profoundly self-destructive aspects of his act. One year later the psychotherapist and the young man could meaningfully consider together the latter's wish to produce a child, illegitimate as he had been illegitimate. At no time in this psychotherapy process was there ever an open discussion of the incestuous implications of this patient's behavior, of the young man's almost conscious wish that the girl's mother would surprise him and see him in the actual act of sexual intercourse. With this emotionally fragile patient, to bring such primitive feelings to direct consciousness would invite a disruption of the psychotherapy process.

Most inpatient adolescents cannot consider such markedly disturbing murderous, incestuous or incorporating impulses in the psychotherapy treatment process unless these teenagers are overtly psychotic—or unless they have sufficient ego strength to be well along in a classical analytic process and thus, by definition, not requiring an inpatient treatment program. By the use of metaphors, humor, and displacement maneuvers in the psychotherapy discussions, the adolescent and the psychotherapist provide and maintain necessary emotional distance devices through which the teenager can sustain and can integrate the ongoing interpretive treatment process. To allow the sensitive adolescent greater comfort in this sharing process the psychotherapist may allow himself to be used as an omnipotent, ego-ideal personification (Easson, 1966).

Most teenage patients can only discuss tangentially or in metaphor their feelings toward the psychotherapist as a real person or as a transference figure. In any open discussion of feelings toward the therapist, direct, angry impulses are much more readily faced and considered by the teenager. This expression of anger still allows the adolescent sufficient emotional distance and adequate independence. The adolescent is liable to flee anxiously and precipitously from any conscious consideration of warm, positive feelings toward the psychotherapist; such an open discussion of caring feelings is liable to be seen as seductively over-close and as inviting a dependent or a homosexual relationship.

> Why don't you take the gun home and give it to your son? I'm sure a little boy like that would have an awful lot of fun with a B-B gun. You can take him down the basement, set up a target and really play with it all night together.

In this way, an outwardly arrogant, supremely self-sufficient teenage boy brought a B-B gun as a gift to his psychotherapist. To the other members of the treatment team, this adolescent presented himself as disdainfully aloof, totally self-adequate, and completely sure of his own masculinity. In a treatment response to this outwardly warm gesture, the psychotherapist began to discuss with him how the teenager himself had practiced with a gun when he was younger. Together the boy and his therapist talked in detail over many weeks about the pleasures of such an experience—the joys of mastery of such a powerful weapon and the fear of such potential destructiveness. Gradually the young man was able to consider how he had hoped desperately for a closer relationship with his father whom he worshiped and idealized at a distance. In the ongoing psychotherapy process, this adolescent had to mourn the loss of the close dependency relationship for which he yearned, both with his own father and with his psychotherapist. In this mourning-transition stage of necessary emotional development, he was helped and encouraged by the psychotherapist to make a wider use of more appropriate peer relationships. As the young man talked longingly of his past hopes, he was able to consider the possibility of now hunting with his peers.

At no time in the psychotherapy process was the young man's wish to be the therapist's little boy discussed. To interpret such a hope would leave this proud young man feeling emotionally stripped and naked. At no time in the treatment discussion was the teenager able to consider his barely concealed murderous wishes toward the people who were not giving him all the love he desired. By bringing this gun into the treatment process, the teenager himself provided a therapeutic metaphor around which a wide range of feelings could be discussed and integrated in a most meaningful, growth-promoting fashion.

115

In the residential milieu setting, the whole treatment team is involved in a constant supportive psychotherapy process but it may be important to give the disturbed adolescent an individual psychotherapist for a specific supportive psychotherapy program. Where the adolescent patient is confident and assured that he has for himself such individualized, personal interest, his psychotherapist can then be very supportive and very direct with the teenager. In any supportive psychotherapy process, the psychotherapist strengthens the emotional defenses the patient already has and tries to make less maladaptive the inefficient reaction patterns the teenager shows. In this basically trusting relationship, the psychotherapist in his role as the patient's special ally can point out to the grandiose teenage patient that, if he proclaims too loudly that he is a world boxing champion, other people will think he is "crazy" and will lock him up—and since the young man does not want to be locked up, to avoid this painful experience he should refrain from expressing his omnipotent, grandiose delusions too openly. In this supportive psychotherapy process, the psychotherapist does not directly interpret the delusion because this teenager does not have the ego strength that could tolerate or use such an interpretation.

In a continuous supportive psychotherapy relationship, the psychotherapist can train the teenage patient in the most simple techniques of relating. Many disturbed adolescents are too shy or too sensitive to admit their social inadequacies in the open residential setting but they can deal with these handicaps very gently and very slowly within the privacy of their individual psychotherapy appointments. The psychotherapist may thus find himself teaching the psychotic or grossly immature adolescent 18 year old young man how to eat in a socially well-mannered fashion. By repeated instruction and direction, the psychotherapist may coach his patient how to function in the ordinary school classroom setting. Because of their emotional handicaps, many teenage patients lack the sensitivity to ordinary social nuances. In a supportive psychotherapy process these adolescents can be directly taught to look for and to appreciate environmental cues and to use these guide lines to structure their behavior in ordinary social settings. In his therapy notes a psychotherapist wrote:

> John is going to his first high school game tonight. We started planning for this game five months ago when he entered summer school. For weeks now, we have plotted and planned how he would go to the game with his peer group. He has now decided to sit fairly high up in the stands so that he can watch the people in front of him and thus learn from them how to react and when to react. He has decided, for this occasion, that he had better under-respond so that he does not find himself busily cheering or shouting abuse when everyone around him has become silent. He remembers only too well how he over-applauded at a recent community concert.
> We have considered his wardrobe together and have planned what he should wear so that he will not appear too conspicuous but yet sufficiently stylish to be attractive. If this outing is successful, John plans next to attend a school dance.

From their own personal psychotherapists, many more disturbed adolescents can use this type of learning experience which they could not tolerate in the more open residential setting. In this treatment process also, the psychotherapist allows himself to be a readily available relationship model.

Although this supportive psychotherapy discussion can be very direct and very specific, for many more disturbed adolescents the treatment process is maintained in a constant treatment metaphor.

> After four years now, Dick and I have come to the end of the Civil War—I think. During all this time, we have spent the large part of our three times a week psychotherapy sessions playing out a Civil War with toy soldiers. At times this War has represented the conflict going on within Dick himself, where love and hate fought each other. At other times, the bloody battle was representative of the struggle within this teenager's family, with his loyalties being dragged first toward his father and then toward his mother. Frequently too, the battle represented the chaos Dick sees in the big, wide world outside of the psychotherapy sessions.

This treatment process has been maintained and discussed solely in terms of generals, armies, individual soldiers, and campaign plans. Whenever a direct interpretation has been made from the ongoing battle process, Dick has become so emotionally disrupted by this interpretation that he has usually followed such a treatment move with several weeks of total silence in the psychotherapy hours. Within this more tolerable metaphor of the Civil War, Dick has been instructed and supported in handling his feelings and in dealing with the disturbing relationships he maintains. We have considered at length how individual generals could plan their campaign strategy and Dick has taken this discussion into his everyday living in a most productive fashion. As the armies have settled their battles and have decided on a peaceful compromise, so Dick himself has found a working settlement in his own inner drives. He finally told me this morning, "I think the Civil War is now over for good. I am bored of playing with soldiers."

In the usual psychotherapy process with the disturbed adolescent, the therapist most often moves backwards and forwards from a supportive to an interpretive approach in response to the needs of the adolescent patient. If the disturbed teenager does grow and show emotional shifts in his treatment process, his therapeutic prescription will have to be changed and adapted. This treatment change may come within the existing psychotherapy relationships or a different treatment process may have to be prescribed. Constantly the whole therapeutic program must be geared to the individual needs of the adolescent.

THE PSYCHOTHERAPIST AND THE HOSPITAL UNIT ADMINISTRATOR

In some residential treatment units, all adolescent patients in psychotherapy have a psychotherapist who is a staff member other than their hospital unit doctor. In other treatment settings, the ward doctor is also psychotherapist for all the teenage patients on the unit. Each treatment approach is beneficial in some ways and has drawbacks in other directions. It should be possible to prescribe the form of psychotherapy approach the adolescent can use, based on his individual needs. Ideally the disturbed adolescent who requires specific psychotherapy treatment should have the treatment option of having a separate psychotherapist and hospital administrator or a combined psychotherapist-administrator treatment relationship. The effect of these two different treatment approaches depends on the emotional strengths of the individual patients and on the total team support and understanding.

In any treatment setting, the therapeutic staff and the patients soon evolve a hierarchical structure in the treatment personnel. Where there are several psychotherapists, very soon these therapists are categorized in the minds of the teenage patients and of the caring staff in order of seniority, effectiveness, competence, and sensitivity. When a specific psychotherapy assignment is announced, the staff reaction will soon convey to the teenage patient whether he is expected to benefit from such a treatment relationship. The look of pity by the child-care worker who discusses the new psychotherapist with the teenage patient will totally undo his consciously verbalized expression of enthusiasm. To the teenage patient and to the staff, it may appear—whether this is a management reality or not—that certain psychotherapists are assigned the less glamorous, less hopeful patients. To be assigned to such a psychotherapist thus becomes a bad prognostic sign to everyone including the teenager who has just been assigned. Where such treatment stratification and expectation seems to have occurred, this management problem must be discussed openly with the patient, the therapists, and with all staff members. If this situation is not dealt with directly, the adolescent patient may be handicapped further by a culturally despised treatment process.

Where the hospital unit administrator is also the adolescent patient's individual therapist, that teenager is likely to be viewed as a special patient by the treatment team. Other caring staff may hesitate to deal realistically and firmly with this particular adolescent because they see the teenager too much as an extension of the administrator. Sometimes it may be felt and even said openly that this adolescent is favored by the administrator or that this teenager can "get away with" things that other adolescent patients can not. Staff and patient feelings toward the administrator may be expressed toward his psychotherapy patients either because the administrator is so weak that the staff feel he could not tolerate such anger or because he is felt to be overly aggressive in face of questioning.

Beck, Macht, Levinson, and Strauss (1967) discuss the problems of the therapist-administrator split in dealing with schizophrenic patients. They suggest that schizophrenic patients who are treated under such a treatment split do not progress as rapidly as schizophrenic patients whose hospital administrator is also their psychotherapist. They believe that the treatment split perpetuates personality fragmentation in these psychotic patients. In their group, patients with character disorders or with depressive reactions were not adversely affected by a split. We would agree with their general conclusions but would add that, for certain specific adolescent patients, for clearly defined reasons, a separate assignment of psychotherapist and of hospital administrator is beneficial. For the deeply psychotic adolescent, a psychotherapy relationship separate from his relationship with a hospital administrator allows him to keep crazy feelings, impulses, and ideas within the circumscribed area of his psychotherapy process. Where a markedly psychotic adolescent has as his hospital administrator the same person who is also his psychotherapist, it is questionable whether he will have sufficient emotional structuring and ego strength to contain his more disruptive feelings within the separate psychotherapy process; florid primitive psychotherapy material is liable to erupt in the day-to-day patient-administrator relationship. A separated psychotherapy process might be prescribed to allow such a psychotic teenager to begin to face and to handle these deeply disturbing feelings within the more controlled, more limited psychotherapy sessions.

For the infantile adolescent patient who relates only at a preambivalent level, a therapist-administrator split has both treatment benefits and drawbacks. Where there is this separation between the role of psychotherapist and administrator, the infantile adolescent can enter more easily into a psychotherapy relationship where he can see the psychotherapist as being all good; he then tends to view the hospital administrator as all bad. Such an immature teenager may be unable to use an ambivalently perceived relationship since he does not have the personality strength to handle such obviously conflictual feelings. Where there is the separate treatment role of psychotherapist and administrator, the treatment team must make sure that this splitting is not solidified in the treatment process. The therapist and the administrator must work together so that eventually the infantile adolescent grows to see human beings as having both good and bad qualities. The paranoid uncertain teenager may find it easier to enter a psychotherapy relationship with a separate psychotherapist in whom he can confide privately and secretly; his paranoid suspicions might make it impossible for him to deal in any intense relationship with a therapist who is also his reality-based administrator.

As with all forms of treatment directed toward the disturbed adolescent, the therapeutic approach must be prescribed in an individual fashion based on an understanding of the needs of each teenager and on the capacity of the treating environment to maintain such a treatment program. There is no one specific treatment approach for the disturbed adolescent but rather each teenager must have in his own way an individualized program geared to strengthen his individual capabilities.

Chapter VI

The Use of Medication in the Residential Treatment of the Disturbed Adolescent

In the total integrated treatment program for the disturbed teenager, the use of medication can be a most useful therapeutic measure when this drug therapy is prescribed with due regard for the needs of the individual patient and the treatment group. While the specific pharmacological effect is extremely important to consider in this prescription, the psychological effect and significance of such medication may have an even more potent result with the teenage patient. These pharmacological and psychological effects may greatly enhance or may counterbalance each other. Medication that is usually helpful for most patients may be totally untherapeutic for certain disturbed adolescents, due to specific drug manifestations or to individual psychological significance. In dealing with the emotionally fragile teenager, the prescription of medication must be very carefully considered with an understanding of each adolescent's emotional strengths and defense patterns (Kraft, 1968).

THE EMOTIONAL EFFECTS OF MEDICATION

The disturbed teenager who is admitted to an inpatient setting is anxious, untrusting, and fearful. He does not have complete control of his own feelings and drives. Usually he has only an uncertain concept of his own physical body and a fluctuating control of his own physical capabilities. By repeated bitter and painful experiences over the years he has learned never to trust completely; he has been taught never to cooperate fully lest he be hurt or controlled against his will. The medication-treatment interaction depends on the specific drug being given to the adolescent patient and on the individual adolescent patient taking this medication. The drug experience is fraught with risks for the uncertain teenager. As he takes this prescribed medication, he must allow himself to trust some vague authority figure who has manufactured the drug. As he has grown, the disturbed teenager has learned to beware of authorities, both parental and social. Now in this medication he is being given, he is asked to allow himself to be openly influenced and controlled medically by authorities. Before he accepts medication from a staff member, the teenager must decide whether he can trust the benevolence of this one adult. The disturbed adolescent has learned that caring people have tended to hurt or to cause pain in an unpredictable fashion; he has found that his behavior caused outwardly supportive adults to reject and to attack him. When the uncertain teenage patient allows himself to ingest or to internalize the medication, he is aware that in some fashion his whole being will be affected—he will indeed be controlled even though he may both desperately fear and wish control. The drug-treatment experience is an intensely invested interaction in social trust, interpersonal trust, and self-trust (Rae-Grant, 1962; Fish, 1968).

The adolescent who is admitted to the inpatient setting tends to have only a very diffuse self-image and incomplete bodily control. The drug experience may face him with new and anxiety-provoking changes in his inner sensations and perceptions. Even minimal variations in his inner physiological status may cause the uncertain self-concept of the more disturbed teenager to fragment disruptively.

A 15 year old boy was started on 50 milligrams chlorpromazine three times a day because of mounting anxiety. After only two doses of this tranquilizer, he erupted in panicky shrieking. From his darkened room, he screamed along the hallway, "I don't like your pills. I don't know what they do to me—it's like they're splitting me up. That's it, I feel I'm being pushed apart." Until he was given the tranquilizing medication, this young man had been just managing to hold himself together. With the increased self-uncertainty caused by the barely perceived inner-physiological changes, he no longer had sufficient personality strength to integrate a definite concept of his self as a solid physical entity.

Many of these uncertain, insecure teenagers feel that the drug experience is an active intrusion into their ego privacy and into their own inner world. Though outwardly they may have cooperated by taking the medication, they may feel that in some way their personality integrity has been violated by an outsider. The giving of drugs may be perceived as a destructive, an aggressive, or a sexualized assault. The paranoid teenager may disrupt emotionally in florid projective thinking, under the emotional impact of the medication he has taken into his self.

> When you guys don't like a person, you put him on this stuff. It makes him quieter so he will take your guff. You can brainwash him easier. You can run him but you're not going to run me. I know you have it in for me. You've been planning it all along. For days you've been watching me and now you think you've got me. I'm not going to swallow your pills. You're just a bunch of queers!

Where the anxious teenager struggles with his ambivalent wishes for dependence and independence, the giving of drugs may be seen by him as a staff method to force dependency and to curb self-sufficiency. The teenager may then have to over-emphasize the fact that he is indeed independent and separate. He may have to demonstrate to the treatment staff and to himself that he is really self-sufficient. Other disturbed adolescents view drugs as potent magical forces. As they swallow their medication, they may fantasy themselves as being endowed with omnipotence and invulnerability. Since these drugs are viewed by some teenagers as containing the real source of adult potency, they may be secreted and stored as a storehouse of potential power and mastery. Some adolescent patients gloat over their collection of pills as would a miser over his gold. With such

124

fantasied treasures of power, the sick adolescent can use his hoarded medication to act out his conflictual impulses. Angry, destructive and depressive feelings can be expressed through the suicidal swallowing of an accumulated pill collection. Attacking paranoid and vengeful impulses can be directed toward peers by providing fellow teenagers with these potent pills. Conflicts with staff members and with adult authority figures can be demonstrated by the illicit or the antisocial use of drugs when these medications are combined with alcohol, soft drinks, or other medications in a drunken binge or in a covert "freak out."

The method of giving medications has a marked emotional significance for each adolescent patient and for the patient group. For many disturbed teenagers, the injection of a drug is considered to be a highly active physical-sexual assault. Frequently this method of receiving medication is heavily charged in the adolescent mind with homosexual and punitive overtones. With the actual injection, pain is inflicted by the injecting staff member on these adolescents who have so little ability to tolerate physical or emotional discomfort.

The use of liquid medications with a disturbed adolescent frequently has a strong regressive emotional significance. Liquid preparations can be sucked and swallowed slowly; they can be retained in the mouth and relished or abhorred. Nasty tasting medications can be given brutally undiluted in a punishing, attacking fashion by staff members. Liquid preparations can be swallowed in such a fashion that the diluting liquid is drunk but the heavier medication is left on the bottom and the sides of the container. Many adolescents soon learn that with certain mixtures, the medication precipitates out or sinks to the bottom so that the drug preparation can be selectively discarded or hoarded.

With pills, tablets, or capsules, the adolescent patient can most readily act out disruptive emotional impulses. These solid drug preparations are readily secreted in the corner of the mouth, in the hair or in any body crevice. Pills can be stored for long periods in an easily concealable fashion. When the teenage patient wishes to discard medication, he soon learns that pills can be most easily pushed into vents, drains, discarded food, or almost anything with which he comes into contact.

In the medication experience, the emotional approach of the treating staff is vitally significant. In residential settings oriented almost completely toward a psychotherapeutic approach, too often the giving of medication is considered a gesture of hopelessness. Where the treating staff so overvalue the psychotherapeutic approach, the staff attitude toward medication may undermine the effectiveness of any drugs given. The adolescent patient quickly senses the staff expectation for treatment results from any drug prescribed. In certain residential units which pride themselves in being "dynamically oriented," the psychological dynamics underlying the staff use of medication render such medication either useless or even harmful.

> Does this mean you're giving up? Only the real sickies have to take this stuff, the guys who just don't have what it takes. Is this all you can do?

In this anxious fearful fashion, an immature adolescent boy questioned the drugs that had just been prescribed for him. From his peers and from certain treatment team members, he had been given the impression that medication was used only when all other treatment methods had failed. If this treatment attitude amongst the patients and the staff had not been corrected, the use of medication with this young man and other patients would have led to an increasingly hopeless, depressed attitude which would have prevented any beneficial drug effects and also undermined the many treatment advances he had already made.

With necessary awareness of the individual and group significance of drugs to the patient in the adolescent unit, both the teenage patient and the treatment staff should be involved in the planning and the prescription of any medication. The purpose and the function of each drug should be considered with the teenage patient who is to have this treatment. Though he must not be burdened with details of esoteric side effects, the treatment rationale and the function of the prescribed medication should be discussed with him. In this integrated treatment process, the prescribing physician must consider with the adolescent patient how together they can work out the optimum program of pharmacological support for the teenager. As in any other treatment approach, the final efficacy of a specific medication is dependent to a large extent on the understanding and the cooperation of the disturbed adolescent for whom the drug is prescribed.

The following physician's notes describe one stage in the necessary treatment alliance with a paranoid schizophrenic 17 year old boy.

For the past few weeks, Jerry has been increasingly anxious. His tension is now reaching the point where he cannot fully control his impulses and where his behavior is becoming increasingly regressed. He is tending to withdraw more and more to his room so that he is cutting off his social contacts. It seems reasonable to prescribe a moderate dosage of chlorpromazine to bring his anxieties to a level that he can manage.

This morning I sat down to discuss the whole situation with Jerry. I pointed out to him how, in recent weeks, his emotional burden had been increasing due to his new school responsibilities and to his difficulties with his family. We talked openly and directly about how he has been showing increasing signs of strain, especially in the last three days. I told him that I felt it was not fair to him that he should continue to suffer this burden of pain and anxiety. I said that I would like to prescribe a course of drug treatment to bring his inner anxiety to a bearable level. Jerry quickly became most defensive. He complained bitterly that I must see him as hopeless and weak. With concrete examples from what he has achieved over the past few months, I reassured him that I very much admired his active attempts to cope and to master and I congratulated him on his achievements. I pointed out that, at this time, he seemed to be pushing himself unreasonably. Though this reassurance somewhat mollified Jerry, his paranoid suspicions soon came to the surface once more. In our discussion he became more and more distant and increasingly vague. He even got up from his chair beside me to sit at the other side of the room. I pointed out these signs of mistrust and inner anxiety, reemphasizing that he and I must think this situation through together.

I assured him that I saw this drug prescription as only a temporary measure. Together we began to plan how he could start at a moderate drug level which he and I would alter on a day to day basis, based on the effect. We talked quite openly about how in the beginning Jerry might feel somewhat sleepy—which would be a drawback in school but would help him settle at night. Jerry is willing to try this tranquilizer but undoubtedly is still most anxious, uncertain and suspicious.

Medication should always be considered as one very useful form of external ego support that can be provided by the treatment team. For certain more disturbed adolescents who maintain a continuously high level of inner anxiety or who possess only very limited ego capabilities, it may be necessary to continue with a drug regimen for an indefinite period. For most teenage patients, drug therapy is prescribed for a time-limited purpose and this prescription is discontinued or changed as the teenager's emotional status changes.

At all times in residential treatment, the treating team must maintain the therapeutic alliance in every area; pharmacological agents must be used with a helpful purpose to augment the strength and the drive of the adolescent patient. Some drugs are advertised as being tasteless and odorless with the implication that they could be given to a patient without his awareness. While such surreptitious medicating may produce short-term symptomatic improvement, in the long run this kind of deceitful treatment approach may lead to therapeutic disaster. The disturbed adolescent normally distrusts, so medication should always be presented openly and discussed as a necessary measure to help him cope in a more productive fashion. The total treatment program for the disturbed adolescent must be geared to promote interpersonal trust, self-awareness, self-control and self-confidence. Secret medication of food undermines basic treatment trust and depreciates what personal strengths and relationship capabilities the teenage patient and the staff members have. These disturbed adolescents are striving to orient themselves to their own bodies, to their environment, and to their inner impulses and perceptions. If they are given any medication unknown to them, they find that their inner sensations are changing for no obvious reason. They know that something is happening to them, they sense a change but they can perceive no reality-based cause. Such covert medicating produces an increased loss in reality contact, diminishing self-confidence, and mounting basic distrust. When treating staff members try to give patients medication without the patient's knowing, this staff action is often the outward expression of unresolved angers and anxieties within the treatment team. The caring staff, in such an instance, must clarify to themselves what there is about this specific teenager or about the total treatment situation in the hospital unit that causes such unproductive and untherapeutic staff behavior.

The Pharmacological Effects on Specific Teenage Emotional Patterns of Behavior

The disturbed adolescent who has been admitted to the inpatient setting, usually has difficulty in maintaining complete reality contact. He may be uncertain about his own ego boundaries and about his own body image. Any drug prescribed, even simple aspirin or a mild laxative, may have a profound and pervasive effect on his total personality integration.

Medication may be prescribed specifically to lower tension in a teenage patient because his inner anxiety is causing increasing personality fragmentation. While this tranquilizing medication may indeed lower his inner tension level, the sedative effects of the drug may further blur his ego boundaries. Even though his inner impulses are becoming more controllable due to the drug, he may find that his sense of self, his personal integrity, and his emotional integration, are being undermined by the relaxing, tranquilizing effect. Many severely disturbed adolescents do not have a clear concept of their own physical body or of their sexual role. They need a constant sensory feedback of external physical sensation to solidify for them their awareness of their physical integrity. Under the quieting influence of a drug, necessary external stimuli may become muted. The poorly integrated adolescent may find that his body image is becoming increasingly vague to the point where he feels that he is tending to merge with his environment. In the face of this increased ego fluidity produced by a supposedly tranquilizing medication, his ego anxiety may disrupt in an uncontrollable panic. Though the drug may have relieved one form of anxiety, it may also so weaken necessary emotional guidelines that the teenage patient disintegrates emotionally under the influence of the tranquilizer.

By the effect of medication on their individual conflicts and unresolved struggles, teenage patients may be both helped and emotionally injured. Many teenagers who are hospitalized have only minimal control of their impulses. Among the numerous drugs used in psychiatric practice, a not uncommon side effect is the appearance of uncontrolled movements. The onset of an akathisia or a dyskinesia syndrome may raise so much anxiety in the emotionally fragile adolescent that his continued treatment progress is disrupted. Where this adolescent has been trying so hard to control his impulsive actions, he now finds, under the influence of a drug, that his movements have become uncontrollable, as a result of which his anxiety mounts and his behavior becomes more disruptive and more regressed. In the adolescent boy who is uncertain of his own masculine identity, the development of gynecomastia during a drug program may produce unbearable anxiety. Where the infantile or the psychotic teenager has only uncertain contact with his environment, the visual blurring caused by medications may produce an increasing disruption of his reality ties. Many paranoid, overly sensitive adolescents feel victimized and righteously indignant when a supposedly helpful drug makes them susceptible to an agonizing sunburn thereby limiting their participation in summer activities.

All caring staff must be constantly alert for medication effects, both typical and atypical, which increase the emotional burden of the individual teenage patient. While drug side effects are not totally avoidable, these complications should be explained as fully as possible to the teenager whenever they occur. Though all medications have some specific treatment effect, in inpatient treatment many drugs have their greatest therapeutic usefulness when the medication is used as a vehicle for interaction between the teenager and the treatment staff. The giving and the receiving of medication forces the teenage patient and the treatment team to relate together in a fashion that has unavoidable significance for everyone involved. For some adolescent patients, the drug experience is the first trusting interaction that they have permitted. From this concrete experience of trust, deeper more meaningful trust and greater self-confidence may eventually be built.

The Drugs Used in the Adolescent Residential Setting

Teenagers tend to be a physically healthy group. The adolescent culture favors active interaction which promotes continued good health. In an adolescent inpatient setting however, many of the disturbed teenagers share their inner feelings through the outward expression of physical complaints. Mounting anxiety within the treatment group may be heralded by an increasing number of requests for aspirin for headaches or ointments for bodily pains. Aggressive teenage tensions may be somatized in muscle pains which require liniments for relief. Inwardly directed teenage anger and aggressiveness may be manifested by the sore that is repeatedly picked or the wound that is continually reinfected. The adolescent who is struggling with his inner feelings of inadequacy may achieve the necessary therapeutic support when he is given care for the sprained joints and the wrenched muscles he somehow develops. Increasing physical awkwardness, repeated fractures or multiple injuries may signal a mounting tendency for self-destructiveness in an individual adolescent. Amongst the adolescent girls, complaints of recurrent menstrual pain may allow the young woman to be cared for in the fashion she craves or these monthly discomforts may be an outward expression of discomfort and uncertainty in her feminine identity.

Even though the adolescent inpatient does tend to express inner anxieties through physical symptoms, it must be remembered that teenage patients are also subject to realistic physical pains and diseases which require physical as well as psychological treatments. It must be kept firmly in mind that even disturbed adolescents can become physically ill and that an abdominal pain may be the expression of a developing appendicitis as well as an unresolved dependency need. During times of heightened emotional tension, there is a slackening of emotional resiliency resulting in lowered physical resistance and a greater likelihood of recurrent winter colds, influenza epidemics, or gastrointestinal upsets.

A residential unit for teenage patients requires an adequate range of simple symptomatic medications. Since many members of the treatment team will not be medically trained, the number of potent drugs on the treatment unit should be kept to a minimum. It is preferable to have one drug which can be used flexibly rather than several medications which serve the same purpose. At all times a physician should keep a close check on the method of drug administration and on the effects of these medications on each individual patient.

The Tranquilizing Drugs

Ataractic medication is given to bring the inner anxiety of the disturbed adolescent within bearable levels. The treatment goal is to reduce the inner tension level of the teenage patient to a point where he can cope with his inner pain and continue to use his energy for growth. Tranquilizers are not given to make the teenager totally unanxious or to render him completely bearable to those around him. Tranquilizers must not be prescribed to anesthetize the adolescent patient emotionally or to render him absolutely predictable. Such blanketing tranquilization would tend to push the uncertain teenager into a distorted, medicated twilight where his reality ties are minimized and his interpersonal relationships reduced to a vague shadow.

In a residential setting, chlorpromazine has been found to be the tranquilizing drug most suitable for general use because this medication is available in a wide range of therapeutic doses and in different forms. The teenage patients and the treatment staff can more easily become acquainted and comfortable with this kind of medication which can be given with readily comparable effect in liquid, capsule, pill, or even injectable form. The therapeutic team members and the adolescent patient group can learn by repeated experience what to anticipate from the drug. Though more potent medications, such as trifluoperazine, are sometimes needed clinically for more pervasive acute anxiety states, in most treatment situations it becomes too easy to raise the treatment dose of trifluoperazine to a level where there occur side effects that are extremely disturbing to the adolescent patient. The prescription of additional antiparkinsonian drugs tend to confuse both the teenage patient and the treating staff. A moderately potent drug, such as chlorpromazine, can be more easily maintained in a treatment program lasting months or years whereas the stronger tranquilizers are more prone to have undesirable and unexpected side effects over this more extended period of dosage. Chlorpromazine can be of benefit on a short-term symptomatic basis, but one of the minor tranquilizers, such as chlordiazepoxide, may also be useful at these times.

The adolescent may require minor brief sedation to handle the temporary anxieties of a parental visit, of new school responsibilities or of periodic menstrual discomforts. Often in these tension-provoking situations, tranquilizing medications are therapeutically useful both for their pharmacological effect and also as a means whereby the anxious teenager can call on personal support from the therapeutic team. While the drug itself undoubtedly relieves tension, the use of "people power" may be even more strengthening and more anxiety relieving. In the residential setting, there appears to be no place for very mild tranquilizers in the meprobamate therapeutic range. Minimal tension states, which might be alleviated by such medications, can be better handled through direct staff support.

The Antidepressant Drugs

In the inpatient setting, antidepressant medication has an uncertain place. Since these drugs take several weeks before the maximal therapeutic effect is supposed to occur, it is difficult to ascertain whether any clinical improvement is due to increased staff support or to the drug itself. Frequently the antidepressant medication seems to provide merely a vehicle for increased staff concern, support, and understanding. Under the guise of this medication, the adolescent patient may more easily accept direction, care, and support without feeling unbearably dependent or controlled. Due to the side effects of antidepressant drugs, the depressed adolescent may be rendered more uncomfortable, more anxious, and more uncertain. If the disturbed teenager is living in the ego void of an anaclitic depression, the stimulant effects of the tricyclic antidepressants may cause totally disabling, disruptive anxieties. If antidepressant drugs are used at all with grossly disturbed teenagers, these medications should be prescribed only with endogenous or reactive depressions.

In a residential setting, it is extremely debatable whether the amphetamine compounds have any useful therapeutic value. The stimulant effects of such medications are much more likely to produce paranoid personality disintegration rather than increased ego competency with the disturbed teenager. The stimulant effect of the amphetamines is more prone to overburden the uncertain adolescent rather than to promote increased ability. Where amphetamines are prescribed to reduce appetite and food intake in the obese adolescent, this drug program must be watched very carefully lest the mounting inner tension produced by the amphetamine compound overburden the adolescent patient emotionally. From the news media and from their delinquent oriented peers, many adolescents have learned to associate amphetamines with addiction and with drug binges. Where supposedly benevolent physicians prescribe amphetamines for a treatment purpose, the disturbed adolescent may become confused by this antisocial significance frequently associated with the amphetamine drugs.

Barbiturates and the Sedative Drugs

For the healthy adolescent, a sleepless night is no great handicap. Physically healthy teenagers can go with only minimal sleep for several nights, only to sleep around the clock for several days. With adolescent inpatients, there is little justification for the constant use of barbiturates to produce or to maintain night-time sleep. If the teenage patient is too anxious or too depressed to sleep soundly, his underlying emotional discomfort should be faced and openly treated by the therapeutic team. In general, barbiturates deaden and dampen reality contact. If the adolescent patient is feeling increasingly tense or unbearably sad, his environmental contacts have to be enhanced and supported rather than minimized and decreased by the use of barbiturates. The adolescent patient must learn to relate more productively to people and to use meaningful relationships to complement his own ego strength. The continued use of barbiturates makes it much more difficult for the adolescent patient to sum up enough energy to reach out actively toward his peers and toward staff members. The persistent prescription of barbiturates may be one means also whereby treatment team members can reject and insulate themselves from a disturbing adolescent patient. In any treatment situation the therapeutic purpose of continued medication must always be maintained under close scrutiny.

Like the amphetamines and the hallucinogenic drugs, barbiturates are frequently used in antisocial and delinquent teenage activities. Many sick adolescents do not have the emotional flexibility to understand that drugs like the barbiturates or the amphetamines can be of use in anything other than their well publicized antisocial purpose. When the disturbed adolescent finds that these medications are prescribed to him by supposedly helpful people, he may become confused, more uncertain, and increasingly untrustful. The confusion of our culture then becomes the confusion of these confused teenagers.

ALLIED SOMATIC TREATMENT APPROACHES

For the growing, maturing adolescent patient, electroconvulsive or drug-induced convulsive therapy seems to have little general purpose. With most of these disturbed teenagers who are still showing emotional growth and personality change, convulsive treatment has usually an emotionally disruptive effect. In the rare instance where a disturbed teenager presents with the symptoms of a manic-depressive syndrome, convulsive therapy may be the specific, optimum treatment approach. During their lifetime, these patients may well require repeated courses of convulsive therapy which may have to be initiated in the adolescent decade. Psychosurgical procedures have absolutely no treatment place with the adolescent patient.

The therapeutic team must constantly evaluate every treatment procedure, psychological and pharmocological, as part of the ongoing, integrated therapeutic process. Medications provide a most potent therapeutic tool but such treatment must be purposefully integrated into the ongoing diagnostic and treatment program for each individual teenager. Drugs cannot be prescribed or given in a fashion divorced from the total treatment approach since the effect of such medication is dependent on a multiplicity of physical, psychological, and environmental factors.

Chapter VII

The Severely Handicapped Neurotic Adolescent in the Inpatient Setting

In his effort to cope with the growth anxieties and the emancipation uncertainties of adolescence, the normal teenager makes temporary but extensive use of maladaptive and anxiety-fraught neurotic emotional defenses. Naturally the average adolescent will on occasion deny his feelings of personal inadequacy by being the mouthy braggart. Normally the developing adolescent will tend to over-react to his inner fears by taking undue risks or by being overly independent. In many ways he tries to emphasize to the world and especially to himself that he is not really insecure. Even though he knows the wisdom of such counsel, the normal adolescent refuses to take direction from his seniors. In his profound sensitivity and his deep uncertainty, the average adolescent may react in a most paranoid fashion—with repeated complaints that people, parents, teachers, police and "they," are against him and do not understand him. The normal growing teenager shows his fluctuating inner conflicts and confusions through his outward, uncouth, sloppy appearance for which he periodically overcompensates by being the immaculate fashion plate. Obsessive miserliness alternates with reckless spending. As the average adolescent develops increasing mastery ability and self-confidence, his inner anxiety slowly diminishes and he can then more easily discard these inefficient, neurotic coping mechanisms which have helped him progress through the adolescent decade.

Where the emancipating teenager has only minimal personality strength and where his inner impulses are not fully controlled, neurotic reaction patterns may persist as his main method of coping with inner anxiety and social responsibility; under such circumstances the adolescent emancipation drive will be increasingly limited and emotional growth stunted to an ever-greater degree. The neurotic behavior of the teenager may cause so much environmental anxiety, anger, and rejection that his inner tensions are further heightened, with increased reinforcement for his neurotic behavior. These neurotic behavior patterns limit the social and cultural opportunities the teenager has for wider relationships so that his interpersonal reactions become increasingly growth limiting. If neurotic symptoms are extensive, the neurotic adolescent may be more severely handicapped in his growth task than even the psychotic or the grossly infantile teenager.

Where the disturbed adolescent presents with a pervasive neurotic reaction pattern involving most of his interactions and his efforts to cope, the situation must be closely evaluated to clarify whether this teenager is suffering from a pan-neurosis covering over a deeper psychotic reaction. A pan-hysteria in a teenager may be the surface manifestation of a profoundly egocentric psychotic syndrome. A severely compulsive reaction pattern may allow a deeply disturbed adolescent to give some outward regulation to his inner confusions. A profoundly apathetic depression may allow teenage withdrawal and can cover over a schizophrenic ego-void. Any teenage neurosis that is maintained for more than a few months and that involves a wide segment of the adolescent's behavior must be viewed with marked clinical suspicion.

The severely neurotic young man or young woman may be brought for diagnosis and for treatment only when the adolescent's maladaptive behavior produces profound environmental disruption or where the teenager's inefficient emotional patterns have caused severe personal and intellectual handicapping. Some facets of neurotic behavior tend to make the growing teenager more acceptable to those around him and thus to delay the necessary evaluation or treatment. The compulsive teenager is much more readily predictable than his normal counterpart; he may be the "model" student in his class—he causes absolutely no trouble, always following his rigid patterns. The young lady may appear more feminine and coquettish if she tends to react in a hysterical fashion. If the teenager is anxious and uncertain, he is less likely to be disturbingly arrogant and defiant.

The disturbed adolescent who functions at a neurotic level has at least adequate ego strength to maintain an age-appropriate self-concept and social goals; he has reasonable contact with surrounding reality and maintains a socially acceptable sex role. For certain, specifically selected, neurotic adolescents, residential treatment is the therapeutic program of choice. A severely neurotic teenager should be recommended for inpatient treatment when his neurosis is causing increasing personality stunting and where his environment is tending to perpetuate and to accentuate his neurotic defenses. The neurotic adolescents who should be treated in an inpatient setting have such widespread personality weaknesses and such high titers of anxiety that they develop a neurotic reaction pattern which involves a wide area of their total family, social, and academic functioning; their neurotic behavior has either produced or accentuated an environmental tendency to support and encourage the neurotic behavior. This neurotically oriented environmental reaction makes it increasingly difficult for the adolescent to give up his neurotic defenses. To an increasing extent, the teenager's neurotic behavior is strengthened by a neurotic environment that the adolescent more and more evolves for himself. Residential treatment is prescribed to break this circle of reinforcement and to minimize the secondary gains derived from neurotic illness.

During the adolescent decade, the teenager is normally in a

state of comparative ego fluidity; he is establishing his self-identity and is solidifying his more permanent character structure. Residential therapy is recommended where the neurotic adolescent finds himself with neurotically based identification models, neurotically oriented ego rewards and repeated reinforcement for his neurosis. The neurotic reaction pattern which began as a necessary emotional defense may well become totally ego-syntonic and no longer anxiety provoking as the teenager stabilizes his personality structure. The uncertain, anxious adolescent may ease the anxieties of his ego-inadequacy by stabilizing a fixed, life-long neurotic character pattern.

By maintaining a stable, consistent environment in the inpatient setting, the unpredictability of the adolescent's existence is lessened and environmental stresses are minimized. In the treatment milieu, his neurotic behavior neither brings reward nor does it cause environmental rejection. The emotional gratification from sick behavior is thus minimized but negative reinforcement does not occur. Within the consistent relationships of the treatment unit and, in selected instances, in a psychotherapy relationship, the relationship capability of the neurotic adolescent is promoted and supported. In an ego growth-oriented treatment setting, the neurotic adolescent is encouraged to develop increasing self-confidence and personal integration so that gradually he can relinquish his more maladaptive neurotic behavior.

Depressive Reactions of Adolescence

The growing adolescent is traditionally "moody." In his natural emotional fluidity, the normal teenager rapidly vacillates from profound sadness to marked elation. With his comparative ego-weakness and with the strong instinctual upsurge of puberty, the behavior and the emotional quality of the adolescent is characteristically labile. These mood swings are appreciated as natural emotional fluctuations by the young adolescent and by those around him; natural allowances are made for these personal mood variations in school and in peer groups. A relatively well adapted 15 year old boy made the following statement which could be echoed by most of his peers at sometime during their adolescent years.

> It just seemed hopeless. I had nothing to live for. The telephone poles kept whisking by. I saw a corner coming up ahead and, for a moment, I had the temptation to keep on driving straight on—right into the wall and telephone pole. What the heck? I didn't do it. I figured by next morning things would be happy and bright and they were.

Unfortunately some adolescents do not have the emotional resilience to tolerate these temporary depressions; this individual inability to recover emotionally may account both for the high suicide rate and the high incidence of accidents during the adolescent decade (Balser and Masterson, 1959; Jacobziner, 1965; Glaser, 1965). This natural adolescent *endogenous depression* may be accentuated and perpetuated in some teenagers so that their mood swings may last for days, weeks, or even months. The adolescent girl may find that she is profoundly depressed around the time of her menstrual period and possibly for several days thereafter. The teenage post-viral droopiness may hang on for weeks or months with the young patient. Most of these suffering adolescents do not come to treatment either because their symptom pattern is relatively short-lived or because their emotional difficulties are not recognized; as Toolan (1962) points out, the tendency of the teenager is to act out his elation or depression rather than to show the more easily diagnosed adult affective pattern.

As the normal adolescent is totally involved in living so is he invested in death. The depressive mood of the teenager may be accentuated and perpetuated because these depressive feelings can become increasingly pleasurable and eroticized. Stearns (1955) describes the type of "normal" adolescent who, in a sexualized fashion, so plays with death and gains masturbatory gratification from the pangs of self-hanging, that eventually he kills himself. Keats in his "Ode to a Nightingale" well describes the adolescent involvement with death—

> I have been half in love with easeful Death,
> Call'd him soft names in many a mused rhyme,
> To take into the air my quiet breath;
> Now more than ever seems it rich to die,
> To cease upon the midnight with no pain,
> While thou art pouring forth thy soul abroad
> In such an ecstasy!

With the natural emotional sensitivity and the lability of the growing teenager, the adolescent reacts profoundly to emotional losses, to hopes dashed, and to disappointments. These episodes of teenage *reactive depression* can be temporarily most intense, but usually the buoyant adolescent can quickly establish other object-ties and other compensatory relationships which allow him to swiftly emerge from his depressed state. These periods of reactive depression may be perpetuated and accentuated by constitutional, endogenous, physical, or hormonal factors. Normally, adolescents with reactive depressions are seen only in brief, supportive consultation and do not require the prescription of inpatient treatment. When, however, the depressed teenager lacks the necessary personality capability (Chwast, 1967), an endogenous depression or a reactive depression may deepen into the disabling depressive syndrome most often observed in an inpatient setting, the *anaclitic depression of adolescence* which is more properly described as an *ego deficiency syndrome* (Easson, 1967e). This syndrome of ego inadequacy can arise not only on the basis of a depressive reaction but may occur in other adolescent neurotic states where the teenager's personality is increasingly burdened beyond his emotional capability.

In 1947, René Spitz described the syndrome of anaclitic depression in infants. In these infants, old enough to relate at a primitive, meaningful level to an external object, the loss of the mothering person produced a profound, obtunded, apathetic depression; this infantile depressive reaction could result in permanent ego stunting in these young children if necessary emotional reparative measures were not taken. Before these infants could become liable to an anaclitic depression, the child had to have the emotional ability to relate. Such relationships provided the infant with external ego support, direction, and nurturance. At all stages of human growth and development, where the growing child, adolescent, or adult, separates or is separated from necessary, emotionally essential, ego support, and nurturing, anaclitic depressive reactions can occur. When the developing teenager emancipates from the nurturing, supportive, family-parental unit, he experiences the loss of accustomed ego support and emotional nurturance. If the emancipating adolescent lacks the necessary ego strength and personal integration to maintain his emotional stability in face of this loss of external ego support and direction, he may develop an anaclitic depressive reaction due to this loss of meaningful relationships and to this withdrawal of essential ego strengthening.

Classically, the neurotic adolescent who is likely to develop an anaclitic depressive reaction, has had a very close emotional relationship with one parent or with a parenting sibling, often a twin or an older brother or sister. As the young child has grown toward puberty, he has become largely dependent on this outside person, both for continued emotional gratification and for support and decision making. Frequently this relationship has been based on a very strong narcissistic tie. The parenting-supporting person has been "loved" only because the growing adolescent has felt that he possessed his love object. This quality of relating is very similar to the type of projective identification described by Melanie Klein (1952) in the very young infant. The loved person, by intensive and excessive projective identification with the hopes and the wishes of the growing preadolescent, becomes merely a narcissistic extension of this child, an emotional extension and a personal projection on which the child becomes absolutely dependent. Such a heavily invested relationship which is based almost totally on projected feelings and expectations, does not allow the future young man or young woman a totally meaningful growth experience. The developing child relates only to his own concepts as these feelings are projected in his mind onto this parenting-supporting person. He loves because he feels he possesses the loved person but he does not love for the individual personal qualities of this emotionally invested object. In such a very intense interaction, the adolescent never has had the full opportunity to relate to a real person, ambivalently and realistically cathected. Object relationships, introjects, and identification models are thus almost totally stunted and the teenager's natural emotional growth is markedly limited. This kind of interaction tends to exclude relationships with other people since these other relationships tend to clash with such a narcissistically based overinvestment. In this growth situation, the adolescent may have become emotionally totally dependent on one person for gratification, support, and direction even though this one person may be the focus of a growth limiting interaction.

Until adolescence the patient may have functioned quite comfortably in most growth settings though, frequently in the historical review, there are indications that the growing child did show definite signs of disruptive anxiety or of an inability to cope on an individual basis when he was separated from the nurturing person. With the onset of adolescence, the child then finds himself expected to emancipate. The more he has been dependent on a meaningful relationship, the greater may be his emotional need to separate. In face of his own inner urges and ambitions and in response to family and social pressures, the teenager tries to become independent. When he now attempts to sunder his exclusive emotional tie, he is liable to find that his individual ego resources are insufficient to manage the stresses of independence and to cope with the loss of a very meaningful relationship. The emotionally stunted adolescent feels inadequate, alone, and empty. He experiences a numbing incapacity rather than a depressive sadness. More than neurotic anxiety, he is likely to sense a mounting panic as a result of ego inadequacy. Due to his personality inability, he is prone to subside into a stolid, bland apathy as the only means available to him of coping with his inner turmoil and his now obvious ego-insufficiency. Superficially the emotional response of such a teenager may appear to be a form of negativism but, as the whole situation is realistically considered, the adolescent is found not to be overtly, actively angry or defiant but rather bewildered, confused, and lost. If such a teenager is left untreated, it is likely that he will continue in this persistent torpid state for an extended period. In such an emotional condition he is no trouble—in the words of his fellow patients "he is just not there."

This syndrome of anaclitic depression, due to ego inadequacy and to the loss of an essential relationship, can occur in any adolescent whose personality resources are severely stunted and limited but who still has the capability to relate meaningfully. To some extent, all teenage patients admitted to a residential setting may show this reaction soon after their admission. The treatment with such young men and young women is biphasic. The essential initial task of the residential team is to provide consistent and sufficient external ego support and direction so that the adolescent becomes once more able to cope. If the adolescent is able to successfully reintegrate emotionally, he may then show his previous neurotic behavior, complicated in this instance by the mourning and the depression produced by this meaningful separation into the new hospital environment. Whereas, in his obtunded apathetic state, the adolescent was quiet and untroublesome, he may become bitter, angry, defiant and a nuisance when he is more integrated emotionally and capable of experiencing the natural sadness and anger of the separation-mourning process.

At age 15, John was admitted to a residential unit because his parents found themselves totally unable to maintain him at school or in the family home. He was content to sit at home in his darkened bedroom, to go out to the movies day after day or to follow his twin brother around the city. He refused to go voluntarily to school; when his parents forcibly placed him in school, his behavior was totally nonproductive academically and disruptive socially. He refused to do any work and spent most of his school time abusing his teachers and his peers. On his admission to the hospital unit, John withdrew more and more to his room. His general behavior became heavy and sluggish, his clothing disheveled and colorless and his attitude tired and apathetic. He was "not noticed" on the hospital unit because he gave absolutely no trouble to the staff. As the members of the treatment team commented, they felt like "just dusting him over in the morning and leaving him sitting where he was."

John had grown up the youngest of his mother's four children and the smaller of twin boys. During his early years, his mother had lost through death her dearly loved father and her first husband. She remarried when John was six years old but, between herself and John, there always was a very close emotional tie; the mother readily and repeatedly stated that John was her favorite child. She said that, during the years when she lost her father and her husband, her close relationship with John had "kept me going." John had also been very close emotionally to his twin brother. Because this twin brother always tended to speak for him, John himself did not learn to talk until he was four years old. In kindergarten and in grade school, John and his brother were always together in the same class and tended to sit side by side.

In school, John was no problem until, at age 10, his work began to slump and he started to stay at home more and more because of vague physical discomforts. As he developed into adolescence, John found that his twin brother was increasingly occupied with other people and other interests. John appeared to find more and more difficulty in organizing his life and in fulfilling his teenage responsibilities. On several occasions, he appeared to be confused and without inner direction. To an increasing extent, he withdrew from school and general social activities so that eventually he was almost totally isolated.

Within one week after his hospital admission, John presented the classical picture of an anaclitic depressive reaction, the ego deficiency syndrome of adolescence.

As with Spitz's anaclitically depressed infants and with the anaclitic depressive syndrome at all age levels, the treatment for these ego deficient teenagers is quite specific. Since these adolescents do not have the inherent ego strength to manage emotionally without an external nurturing-strengthening person, they should be provided with such a strong parenting figure. As an essential first step in the treatment program they must immediately be assigned a specific, warm, comfortable, noncompetitive but growth-supporting adult. Though the normal growth task of adolescence is to separate emotionally from the family-parental unit and it might thus be considered therapeutically regressive to reunite the adolescent with his parents, for the anaclitically depressed teenager with the most severe ego incapacity, it might indeed be necessary to re-establish the actual parent-child bond as an essential, but hopefully temporary, regressive treatment maneuver before a growth-separation process can be later established. In the residential treatment setting, more usually a substitute but definite parenting person is provided. Most anaclitically depressed adolescents, with even minimum ego capability and the most limited relationship capacity, are able with total environmental support to use these alternative substitute parents to re-establish their emotional integration. In most instances, the anaclitically depressed adolescent does not have the emotional capacity to use at this early treatment stage a warm supportive psychotherapy process in addition to this close parenting support provided by a specific member of the residential treatment team: at this very regressed stage of relating, the adolescent does not have the capability of interacting with two people. Though such a dual nurturing approach may be beyond the beginning relationship capability of the anaclitically depressed adolescent, as the teenager develops increasing personality strength during the treatment process, a warm psychotherapy relationship may be prescribed later to enhance his individual growth and his personal emotional integration.

At the earliest stages of treatment with the anaclitically depressed young man or young woman, the teenager is not asked to make any decisions or to take any initiative but rather is cared for, supported, and nurtured. The first treatment task is to help the teenager to reintegrate emotionally, albeit on the basis of an anaclitic relationship. Once the adolescent has re-established some emotional cohesion, gradually and very slowly over months or years the members of the treatment team support his personality growth toward the goal of separation and self-sufficiency. While most adolescents with this minimal capacity to relate in an anaclitic interaction do have the ability and the potential to develop toward final emancipation, a small number of very disturbed teenagers with relatively fixed ego stunting may never be able to function totally on their own and may require a constant, permanent source of external ego strengthening and direction; this personality support may have to be provided in a sheltered hospital environment or in a workshop setting.

The reintegrative and growth support for the adolescent with an anaclitic depressive reaction has to be maintained for an extended period of usually several years, though this support does not of necessity have to be completely within an inpatient setting. If sufficient usable external ego strengthening and nurturing is not provided to the regressed adolescent in his anaclitic depressive state, his withdrawn apathetic reaction may become a fixed character pattern which endures during his adult life; he may remain socially inadequate and permanently handicapped, intellectually and emotionally—dull, "not caring," and obtunded. His intellectual stunting may become so perpetuated and so accentuated that he shows relative or absolute mental retardation at all levels of functioning.

During the anaclitically depressed stage when the teenager shows only apathy, withdrawal, and emotional numbness, the treatment team can easily contain the adolescent's behavior on the residential unit. Once external support and gratification are provided and used emotionally by the disturbed adolescent, he develops sufficient emotional integrity which once more enables him to experience personal anxiety and depression. When the teenager has been successfully helped to recover from his apathetic withdrawal, he is then capable of reacting emotionally to separation and emotional losses. He is now able to feel the angers, the anxieties, and the loneliness of separation; his previous neurotic defenses may now become

148

more obvious and more accentuated as he handles his depressive sadness and anger. In a productive treatment process with such an ego-limited teenager, the therapeutic staff must take care lest this newly aroused depression and tension is not acted out self-destructively nor vented harmfully on those in the environment. The role of the treatment personnel is to help the newly reintegrated adolescent to work through his separation tensions in a growth-productive fashion which will allow him to form compensatory emotional ties.

Rie (1966) with much justification criticizes the labeling of this ego deficiency syndrome as "depressive." When these emotionally limited patients are experiencing their torpid, apathetic state, they lack the basic ego ability to feel depressed. Only when their personality strength increases through their inner growth, or is augmented by external ego supports, can these patients experience meaningful depression; only then do they have the ego capability to feel meaningful object loss and to react with sadness and with anger. The emotional quality of the anaclitic state is predepressive. When external ego support is given to bring about emotional reintegration, the anaclitic teenager can move emotionally to the point where he is liable to act out his newly felt depressive feelings in suicidal or aggressive behavior. Only when added ego support is given and is used can the anaclitically depressed teenager begin to experience meaningfully the anxiety and the bitterness in separation. It must be reiterated and re-emphasized that, during the successful treatment of the teenage anaclitic depression, the ego deficiency state of adolescence, the teenager becomes symptomatically worse as he emerges from his state of anaclitic withdrawal to the emotional position where he can feel and react actively. Anti-depressant medication seems to have little treatment purpose in these ego deficiency states; rather these drugs may add to the emotional burden the teenager must tolerate. Antidepressants seem to be effective only when the patient has a sufficiently capable ego to use the push provided by the medication.

The Severely Disturbed Adolescent
with Phobic Symptoms

Where the growing adolescent has only very limited ego resources, his emancipation-separation anxieties may be well focused in phobic symptoms. The greater stress the teenager is subject to and the weaker his basic personality strength is, the more severe and more pervasive will be his phobias. A disturbed adolescent should be considered for inpatient treatment where his phobic symptoms are causing increasing relationship disruption and where he is so lacking in personality strength that even his phobias are not adequate to contain his total anxiety. The phobic symptoms may lead to social rejection that causes the teenager even more anxiety which is then expressed in wider neurotic reactions. When severe and pervasive phobic behavior patterns are present in the adolescent, marked emotional handicapping is likely to be present. School phobia or separation anxiety in the adolescent is usually indicative of a very uncertain ego state in that teenager. Where phobic symptoms co-exist with other neurotic reactions or with open anxiety, a pervasive emotional disorder may exist.

A behavioral therapy approach (Wolpe and Lazarus, 1966) is usually not fully successful with these more disturbed adolescents. These teenagers lack sufficient personality capability to integrate and to use a learning and a reconditioning experience. When they develop increased ego strength to maintain their own integrated emotional independence, these adolescents can then use a behavioral therapy approach meaningfully and productively. The treatment program with the severely disturbed adolescent must be geared to reduce the stresses to which he is subject, to build up his emotional resources and capability and concomitantly with other treatment techniques to help him give up his phobic reactions and defenses.

No one knows how scared I am of school. When I go into that classroom, a scariness comes over me in waves. I feel that the kids are looking at me and can see right under my skin. Miss Smith has a glassy look in her eye as if I smell nasty. I just want to stay at home and lie in bed with you.

In these words a 14 year old girl tried to describe in her diary some of her phobic feelings about going to school. This young girl, orphaned when she was two years old, had grown up the darling of her doting grandparents. Everything she had wanted she received. Her grandparents had little else to do but to insure that she received constant total affection and warmth. She had progressed through grade school, a charming, intelligent, little girl. When she moved into junior high school, she began to complain of recurrent, vague, physical symptoms. Intensive medical examinations showed no physical basis for her complaints. Eventually she began to stay back from school because she feared the classroom setting. In her own words, she was terrified lest "I go into that room and start screaming and hollering."

A psychiatric examination showed that this teenage girl was very limited in her ego growth and capability. She had grown up much too dependent on her grandparents and on her friends for continued warmth, support, and direction. She did not have the personality capability to become independent at the time of adolescence. Under the emancipation demands of puberty, her ego anxiety had spiraled and had been expressed outwardly in a school phobia symptom.

For two weeks after her admission to the hospital, the treatment unit resounded to her sobs, moans, and protests. She lay in her bed and wept loud and lugubrious tears. She was now too fearful to rise physically from her hospital bed. Her grandparents needed a great deal of support and direction to leave her in this miserable situation. With a great deal of individualized treatment support, slowly and very tentatively the young girl was able to rise from her bed—initially to do simple tasks within her room, then to emerge into the treatment unit and next to go to the hospital school. Gradually, over the next year, she moved back into a public school setting on her own emotional resources and, with continued psychotherapy support, she was transferred to a foster care home.

In the ongoing treatment process with the severely phobic adolescent the therapeutic team must constantly watch for signs of increasing personality disintegration. When a phobic symptom changes into a more unrealistic paranoid reaction, the teenager's emotional strengths are obviously proving less and less adequate. Where the anxious adolescent begins to misinterpret external stimuli to an illusionary extent, his reality ties are clearly becoming more fragile. The treatment team

151

will have to provide increased support for the decompensating patient. Medication may be most helpful in reducing inner tension. In a treatment program, the relationship capability of the phobic adolescent should be actively used from the beginning of the therapeutic process. The phobic teenager is usually capable of using nondemanding emotional supports to minimize inner anxiety and to support personality growth; the long-term prognosis with the phobic adolescent tends to be fairly optimistic but the eventual treatment result depends of course on the inherent ego capabilities of the individual teenager, on his relationship capability and on the continued stresses to which he is subject.

OBSESSIVE COMPULSIVE REACTIONS IN ADOLESCENCE

In his review of psychiatric illness in adolescence, Annesley (1961) states categorically: "Obsessional state is the rarest psychiatric illness in adolescence." The author would disagree most strongly with this statement. An obsessive state may be either a regressive or a growth phenomenon. In any treatment unit for the severely disturbed psychotic or markedly infantile adolescent, an obsessive pattern of behavior is the most common emotional growth phenomenon seen as these teenage patients grow and mature from their very regressed status to a healthier form of adaptation.

As the very severely disturbed adolescent begins to cope with his inner confusion and uncertainty and as he tries to develop a stable relationship with his external environment, he finds it most easy to establish external stability by setting up rigidly compulsive patterns of living. By forcing a rigid predictability on their environment through their compulsive behavior, these adolescents establish for themselves a compulsive, monotonous sameness in their world—but a sameness which they can begin to trust. This environmental constancy allows these emotionally fragile teenagers to bring some stability to their inner impulses and drives. By reducing both their inner and their outer uncertainties to a minimum by markedly compulsive behavior, these teenage patients begin to establish for themselves a modicum of constancy and self-confidence. By insisting on an inflexible sameness in their environment, in their own behavior and in their social interaction, these uncertain teenagers begin to establish for themselves a repetitive constancy on which they can build some confidence. By stabilizing the environmental cues, these teenagers can test for themselves the reality and the appropriateness of their own feelings and their own reactions. If the environment stays the same, these teenagers have the opportunity to vary their reactions and test the effect and the significance of their feelings against a stable background. In this fashion, they can begin to strengthen their reality ties and start to develop increasing self-perception and self-confidence. Where a confused or grossly immature adolescent begins to insist on a rigid patterning and stability in his living environment, the treatment team must view these new obsessive-compulsive defenses as a most healthy and optimistic sign of emotional growth which they should support within all realistic bounds. As these markedly disturbed teenagers develop increased ego capability and self-confidence, they will also evolve more emotional flexibility and more personal capability for tolerating unpredictability in their environment and in their interactions.

Adolescents, who are more grossly disturbed, may never develop sufficient ego strength to allow them to grow beyond this totally predictable state of marked compulsiveness. If the environmental stresses become too great for these limited adolescents, they may show temporary regression to previous psychotic or infantile patterns of behavior. If the emotional burden placed on the patient can be reduced and his compulsive defenses supported and strengthened, this emotional regression may be minimized and reversed. When a disturbed adolescent shows a compulsive behavior pattern as a growth phenomenon, the therapeutic team must support these relatively inefficient neurotic, maladaptive defenses as a necessary transitional stage in the evolution of increased emotional capabilities.

Joshua was 13 years old at the time of his hospitalization. From the day of his admission, his room was a confusion of books, sandwiches, clothes, magazines, candies, fishing rods and other unpredictables. His environmental confusion reflected his inner disorganization. Though he was of superior intelligence, his bizarre and illogical thinking made it difficult for him to maintain himself even on a third grade level in the hospital classroom.

During his third hospital year, it did seem that Joshua was beginning to trust some members of the treatment team. He would allow himself to be touched and to be supported physically during swimming instruction. Occasionally he asked for advice and sometimes he accepted and used the direction he was given. Slowly over this year, his room began to assume an increasingly bare appearance. Eventually his only visible possession was one calendar pinned to his bulletin board. The treatment staff became more and more perturbed at this impoverishment of Joshua's environment until they understood that, in his endeavors to bring organization to his inner confusion and outer environment, this young man had to simplify his living situation in this most rigid, simplified, compulsive fashion.

Over the next two years Joshua's environment reflected his increasing emotional development. On his bulletin board first appeared racing cars then racing heroes. He allowed himself first to relate to the idealized idols and to distant historical personages. During his fourth year in hospital, as he began to take pride in himself as a person, pictures of schoolmates and peers in various friendly poses appeared on his dresser top. When he was about to leave the hospital, after five years, he began to allow himself to decorate his room with self-portraits and with pictures of his family.

As a necessary growth stage in this progression from psychosis to reality-based relationships, it was necessary for this disturbed adolescent to live through a period of many months of rigid, bare compulsiveness.

In the course of a psychiatric examination, when a teenager is shown to have a very wide range of compulsive defenses which have been present for months or years, the diagnostic team must make very sure that these compulsive defenses do not cover over an underlying psychotic disorganization. If the compulsive adolescent is suffering from a deeper, pervasive psychotic state, any treatment program which adds to his emotional stress or which requires ego flexibility, may precipitate ego disorganization and florid psychosis; an interpretive psychotherapy process may cause a covert psychosis to become disruptively obvious and a behavioral therapy approach may overtax the emotional resources of a minimally functioning teenager.

Bill was seen in an outpatient evaluation because of his prolonged, pervasive, and handicapping compulsiveness.

For three years, he had rarely gone to bed until after midnight, because he sat up for hours trying to get his homework absolutely correct and immaculate. Rarely was he able to select his own clothes in the morning because he could never decide what he preferred to wear. He would spend two hours in front of his clothing rack unable to decide which color suited him better. His parents were not aware of any social relationships he had been able to maintain.

The psychiatric examination showed that Bill was of superior intelligence with a wide range of neurotic compulsive defenses; no overt break with reality could be demonstrated. A twice-a-week psychotherapy program on an outpatient basis was prescribed for Bill, with concomitant casework support for his parents.

Bill entered into the psychotherapy process very willingly. He quickly developed a warm, friendly relationship with his male therapist who found the young adolescent to be most attractive. Within two months, however, it became obvious that the teenager's compulsive defenses covered over a marked psychotic state. Within his psychotherapy sessions, the young man began to experience first obvious illusions and then frank auditory hallucinations. He continued to maintain himself appropriately but was socially isolated in school. Since other treatment facilities were not reasonably available, this adolescent patient was maintained in this outpatient treatment process for the next five years. During much of this time the psychotherapist provided constantly available support; the young man had the freedom of asking for extra psychotherapy hours when he felt he required this and could call his psychotherapist outside of these appointments. The psychotherapist learned to organize this young man by telephone when he was called in the middle of a screaming, disorganized panic. By letter, at times on a daily basis, the psychotherapist supported this young man's stability, constancy, and slowly increasing emotional capability.

Though the final treatment result with this young man was very satisfactory, it is a moot point whether he should ever have been started in an outpatient psychotherapy process. In outpatient treatment where environmental supports were minimal, there was a constant risk that this young man would develop an irrevocable emotional disintegration. In a more supportive residential treatment setting, he could have been given the external support and the direction that should have been available to him when his compulsive defenses were being altered and replaced in any reconstructive treatment process.

Other adolescents who have a relatively mature ego capability and integration and a secure sense of personal individuality, may handle the anxieties and the conflicts of their emancipation by the use of neurotic obsessive defenses. These compulsive defenses may be perpetuated and stabilized because these adolescents find such behavior in some way gratifying or even sexually pleasurable. The compulsive teenager may enjoy wallowing in his obsessive ruminations. Repetitive rituals may become a regressed masturbatory pattern. As a 17 year old boy wrote—

Philosophy

As cloud turns to cloud and the mist thickens to deep, dark despair, the murky soup of my emotions clutches me with its soothing, loathing fingers. I drag, and I am dragged, into the mire—into the pit of sorrow and solace. Yet I feel my self-centered vanity, I know of my sin. But where else do I turn—to what other saving portal? In my loneliness and self-sorrow I twitch, writhe, cry, enjoy. And what will come when the emotional numbness wears off? Perhaps more pain—that unbearable, unjustifiable pain—or perhaps a purged soul cleansed for the next battle.

[There can be a great deal of pleasure in "writhing," "unjustifiable pain," and the feeling of those "loathing fingers."]

Where the compulsive adolescent shows by his competent functioning in other social and academic areas that he does indeed have a fair amount of ego strength and relationship ability, the treatment team must face him with the reality that constant obsessions create constant delay. Where the teenager has shown capability in other areas of interaction, he needs to face the fact that his repeated indecision results in continually postponed commitment. As long as his obsessional state is maintained, the maturing adolescent is allowed to avoid complete age-appropriate responsibility. The task of the treatment team is to highlight to the compulsive teenager how much he is handicapped by this obsessive behavior; the caring staff must insure that this compulsiveness does not in its own way provide continued gratification. When the neurotically compulsive adolescent finds that the people in his environment are not going to struggle over his well-publicized agonies, his trumpeted pain and his emblazoned martyrdom, these ever present miseries become much less rewarding. In the treatment setting, the compulsive adolescent is accepted exactly at the level he presents himself and is given the responsibilities and the rewards consistent with this level of functioning. Where the teenager's compulsive symptoms are an outward manifestation in the emotional growth of a formerly psychotic adolescent, this limited responsibility will minimize the environmental demands on this maturing teenager. For the more capable teenager, who maintains a compulsive neurotic pattern because such behavior allows him to avoid responsibility or commitment, this level of limited responsibility and reward is ungratifying; in this fashion these more able adolescents are goaded into relinquishing some of their compulsive defenses and encouraged to grow toward increased responsibility and more mature rewards.

Hysterical Reactions in Adolescence

Hysterical reactions tend to be evanescent and short lived in children and adolescents (Proctor, 1958; Moss and McEvedy, 1966). Only where the ego coping abilities of the adolescent are too limited or where the hysterical behavior patterns have become too gratifying and too egosyntonic, only then should a disturbed adolescent be considered for residential treatment. Where the adolescent patient manifests a wide range of hysterical symptoms, pervading much of his or her functioning, the diagnostic-treatment team must closely evaluate whether such an extensive neurotic symptom merely overlays an underlying psychotic state. In the residential treatment setting, a hysterical reaction pattern may be a necessary growth-transition stage in a previously psychotic or markedly infantile adolescent.

157

A 15 year old girl, who formerly had overt religious delusions that she was herself the Virgin Mary, became a socially accepted wit because of her "joking" religious allusions and comments. Though she no longer claimed that she was the Holy Mother, she would have her schoolmates in fits of laughter with her droll jokes. From her local chapel, she acquired some holy water which she froze and sold around her local school as "pope-sicles." During the school recess, she would ring "Dial-a-Prayer" and then stagger around the hallways claiming that she was "saved." On two occasions she remained immobilized in her bed, under the belief that she was being crucified.

As this young girl grew toward a healthier adjustment, she attended a local revivalist meeting where she was indeed "saved." For months thereafter, her behavior was impeccable and her daily interactions were consistently directed by the effects of this religious conversion. At the time of her hospital discharge two years later, she had developed a remarkable degree of reality contact and emotional flexibility.

During the adolescent decade, teenagers are expected to become adequate and self-sufficient. For this independent role, they require a certain definite ego strength. A hysterical reaction pattern may not only contain the teenager's ego anxieties about personal inadequacies but may also allow this inadequacy itself to become gratifying. The young man, who emotionally cannot stand on his own two feet, may find it not only unnecessary to fend for himself but also socially most rewarding if he develops a hysterical paralysis of a leg. The emotional weakness of this teenager may make it difficult for him to relinquish this symptom in order to assume appropriate responsibilities, and the attention of his peers and his family may render it practically impossible to give up the ailment. Very often, in dealing with disturbed adolescents, the treatment team find that these teenagers have been placed in a situation where they cannot give up a maladaptive symptom without losing too much "face."

John's father was outwardly a sedate country banker but, in his inner dreams, he was a frustrated all-American football player. He gloried in the athletic success of his growing son whom he showered with all kinds of rewards. In his eagerness to keep up with his father's expectations, John focused so much emotional energy and personal initiative in his football endeavors that he tended to isolate himself from his peers. He spent most of his time in football practice but had little experience in ordinary social relationships. He grew into adolescence socially and academically stunted. Unfortunately for this young man, he was late with his adolescent physical growth spurt so that his age peers developed physically well in advance of him. By the time he was 14 years old, John was finding that he could not keep up with his schoolmates socially, academically, or now athletically. To an increasing extent he cringed under the reality that he was not meeting his father's expectations. In a football scrimmage, John fortuitously twisted his ankle. He was carried from the football field by his teammates, his coach, and his solicitous father. Following this accident the father again showered John with the warmth and affection he had shown when John was succeeding so well in grade school athletics.

Several days after John's injury, he was still unable to walk. A thorough neurological examination showed a classical hysterical paralysis of the foot. John's father felt that there had to be some gross neurological lesion to cause this handicap; he felt that his son was likely to be injured for life and so he began an increasingly confused series of medical and neurological examinations. From each examination John and his father received a slightly different report though the basic diagnosis of a hysterical paralysis remained the same. Because of the natural variations in each medical report, John's father still maintained that they must be missing some definite neurological lesion.

Through the ensuing turmoil, John appeared outwardly very tranquil and indeed remained the center of family attention. No longer was he under pressure to shine athletically beyond his capabilities. His friends were now paying him a great deal of attention so that he was beginning to learn some of the social graces he had missed in years past.

In an attempt to "help" his son, John's father began supervising a program of bed-fast exercises. By chance, one evening, the father so strenuously exercised his son that the boy developed pain in his uninjured foot. John thereupon developed a paralysis in that foot also. Further neurological examinations now demonstrated a bilateral hysterical paralysis. Psychiatric examination was recommended at this point.

When it was clarified that John's physical injuries were minimal and that his symptoms were indeed hysterical in nature, residential treatment was recommended. In planning a treatment program, first it was therapeutically necessary to minimize the emotional stresses posed on this young man until his ego capabilities were strengthened further. He needed to develop his inherent potential for social relationships and for reasonable academic achievement before he could be expected to cope fully with the responsibilities of adolescence. John required to be separated

159

from his family environment so that the family support for his hysterical symptoms could be minimized and so that he could give up his hysterical symptoms with minimum loss of self-esteem.

If this adolescent had possessed greater relationship capability, undoubtedly he could have been treated productively on an outpatient basis. A short-term inpatient stay was necessary before he could be moved to a foster home setting and later back into his own family. Intensive casework was required during this whole process to help both parents support the growth of their son's individuality.

As Robins and O'Neal (1953) point out in their review of hysteria of children, the longer a hysterical symptom has been present, the poorer the prognosis tends to be. After several months, a hysterical symptom is liable to become so egosyntonic and so perpetuated by environmental reaction that short-term supportive treatment is usually to no avail. Where a hysterical reaction pattern is maintained in this fashion, one hysterical symptom may respond to treatment, only to be replaced by another hysterical syndrome in the same patient. Where the hysterical symptomatology cannot be totally removed, these patients may have to be helped to live with their hysterical character structure in a nondestructive fashion. They must avoid placing themselves in jeopardy of polysurgery or of potentially harmful multiple medications.

THE CHRONICALLY ANXIOUS ADOLESCENT

In the face of life's demands, the normal adolescent has periodic episodes of anxiety and uncertainty. For most maturing teenagers this ego anxiety is a spur toward further learning, mastery, and growth. For some less capable teenagers, the main method of handling anxiety is to be anxious. This pattern of perpetual anxiety allows the teenager to avoid commitment and final responsibility. If he acts in a consistently inadequate fashion, eventually he is not expected to be adequate. If he portrays himself as a failure, eventually he will be expected to be a failure and thus will not be given too many responsibilities.

Nobody hurts the clown. It's the guy at the top who gets the mud thrown at him. The clown is always safe. He hurts himself a little bit so that nobody hurts him a lot. I play the clown. I am the jester. It is the kings and the lords and the ladies who get their heads cut off. The fool, the jester, the clown lives to a ripe old age.

With these remarkably wise words, a 16 year old young man described the basic reason why he had remained chronically anxious since he moved into puberty. In his school and in his family living, he was now known as and accepted as a "worrier." Amongst his peers, he was felt not to be a threat to anyone and, though he had no leadership responsibility, he was accepted in most social groups as a hanger-on or as one of the crowd of followers. If responsibility had been forced on this young man, he might then have been faced too directly with his ego inadequacy with resultant depression and overt anxiety —on the other hand, he might have been prompted to try even harder and to grow. The chronically anxious adolescent only rarely comes for examination and even less frequently is considered for treatment on an outpatient or an inpatient basis. The anxious, inadequate teenager usually causes no social problems and very often is not considered emotionally ill. Every social group has its chronic follower, its clown, its buffoon, and its failure. As with any other severely handicapped neurotic teenager, any diagnostic examination must clearly evaluate whether this persistent anxiety state underlines a marked ego deficiency. An examination process must clarify whether the neurotic syndrome has become so egosyntonic that it is a fixed and unchangeable part of the adolescent's character structure. Only if the adolescent still feels pain, due to these neurotic symptoms or to his personal inadequacies, can he be helped to make the necessary emotional growth changes that will eventually allow him to relinquish his neurotic behavior patterns.

Chapter VIII

Ego Defects and Developmental Arrest in the Disturbed Adolescent

There is a large group of adolescent patients of normal intelligence and average physical capability who, though they have a definite, stable self-concept, and are aware of basic reality, act in such an inappropriate fashion as to appear "crazy." Diagnostically it is essential to delineate this patient group from the psychotic adolescent as the treatment and the prognosis with these teenagers is very different. These adolescent patients are difficult to diagnose accurately unless the level of their emotional growth and relationship capability is carefully evaluated; from such an examination, it can be shown that, though these teenagers are not psychotic, they show extremely severe stunting of ego growth and severe developmental arrest in relationship ability.

BACKGROUND FACTORS

Most growing children, as they move through adolescence, temporarily show behavioral patterns reminiscent of a much younger age level. This behavioral regression is usually short-lived and is most often seen as a response to unusual stress or excessive emotional strain. To maintain such a childlike pattern of behavior would be too embarrassing for the pride of the normal adolescent. Certain disturbed adolescents do not feel silly or stupid when they show childlike behavior. For them, such infantile emotional reactions are a constant way of life; they have known no other fashion in which to react. These teenagers are the young men and the young women who have never progressed in their emotional development beyond a very primitive and infantile pattern of relating. These teenage patients are not yet completely stabilized in these childlike character patterns because, with the personality fluidity and the emotional energy available with adolescence, they still have some ability to change, to grow and to mature. Interpersonal relationships are meaningful to them, albeit at a very immature level; such relationships may be used to encourage them to grow emotionally in a natural friendship process or in a treatment interaction. In these adolescents, we see the syndrome of developmental arrest where the emotional arrest can at least be partially removed during the adolescent decade, rather than a fixed psychosis or character disorder as is seen in adults.

As they grew through childhood, these disturbed adolescents have been allowed and even encouraged to continue infantile and childlike. In some instances, the parenting adults enjoyed having a child who was irresponsible, dependent, and immature. Such parents found pleasure in the infantile demands of the bosomy 15 year old girl or in the childish frustrated splutterings of the muscular 16 year old boy. Other parents of teenagers disturbed in this fashion have realistically been unable to control or direct their growing child, even when the child was young, so that the youngster had insufficient external support to produce self-control and self-growth. Some of these children seem to have been unusually endowed with strong instinctual drives and energy so that they would be difficult to manage or to train even in optimum home circumstances. With some of these teenage patients, it appears that the parents were well-meaning but lacked the necessary self-confidence to apply realistic controls and direction. Many of the parents of this particular teenage group actually do not know how to give love, control, and appropriate direction to a child; these parents, like Harlow's "Motherless Mothers" (Seay, Alexander, and Harlow, 1964), have not themselves been loved or mothered and so have never trained to be parents; whatever parenting ability they develop they achieve in a haphazard interaction with their children. In the families of all these teenage patients, early in the child's life, there developed a deep fear of mutual destructiveness between the parent and the child—fears that parental controls and angers could destroy the child and anxieties that the child's furies and frustrations could annihilate the parent. These parents never really controlled the growing child either through example or by enforcement. Such family relationships perpetuated the infantile relationships of the future teenager and prevented his emotional growth and development.

Frequently these disturbed adolescents come for diagnosis and for treatment only at the insistence of their community. Many parents continue undisturbed by the teenager's lack of emotional development and give only minimal support to any treatment program. In some of these families, when the adolescent moves actively into pubertal development, he becomes threatening to the family stability by his more obvious sexuality and his more menacing aggressiveness. Where the family could tolerate and did enjoy a grade school infant, they could not quite bear the same pattern of behavior in a sexually potent, physically capable young man or young woman (Counts, 1967).

Syndrome Patterns

You want me to go to school and so do I. You want me to go into Dad's business and so do I. You want me to have fun like any other 18 year old young man and so do I. But, if you don't do what I ask, then I won't go to school, I won't go into the business, and I shall shut myself in my room and do nothing. I don't want to do this. I think it would be a stupid thing to do. But if you don't do things my way, I will!

This is a beautifully presented letter, each point clearly elucidated. The presentation and the format are most appropriate for the 18 year old young man who wrote in this vein to his parents. The message, however, is perhaps more suitable for a 24 or 30 month old child who is proclaiming "If you do not do it my way, I will eat worms and die and you will be sorry!"

> My hair is my business, my clothes are my business. If I want to grow my hair down to my shoulders that is my affair. If I want pointed shoes, that is no one's business but mine. And I darn well plan to grow my hair until it reaches my waist and wear the most pointed shoes I can get!

All that is needed here is a derisive outstretched tongue to complete the picture of a defiant four year old child—except for the fact that this is the statement of a 17 year old boy.

Frequently, these teenagers with emotional developmental arrest present a symptom pattern that suggests a psychotic break with reality. Their outward behavior is so age-inappropriate that they may indeed appear to be deranged. In reality, their reactions are not inappropriate or psychotic when this behavior is considered against their very childlike emotional developmental level. Thus a 15 year old adolescent girl may bleach her hair on Monday, dye it black on Tuesday, bleach it again, dye it gray on Wednesday (rendering it a greenish-gray color), and on Friday triumphantly appear in school with a purple rinse so that her hair is now a rubbery, matted mess. To her school peers, she appears as "nutty"; they react to her appearance with amusement, contempt, and something akin to fear—fear because her behavior is so weird and outwardly so self-destructive. The young adolescent girl, with her hair dyed, bleached, and rinsed, comes and goes—outwardly oblivious to the environmental reaction, almost in a world of her own, almost as if she were autistic. She does not seem to care, she does not seem to feel unusual. Any questions about her appearance may bring the blunt response that "It is none of your business, so why do you worry? It is my hair and I like it this way!"—and so she parades, the object of derision, fear, and pity, isolating herself from those around her. Outwardly she appears crazy; yet her behavior is very reminiscent of the two-year-old child, who, above all else, has to prove herself independent. Such a young child when offered a cookie may verbally refuse it to assert her independence and then, if she is still able, will take the cookie she really wanted all along. This normal 2 year old child was willing and indeed determined to do without the cookie to show that she had indeed "a mind of her own." Some adolescents who have only the emotional development of a two year old will show such social defiance as to appear outwardly psychotic, whereas in reality their behavior is due to their extremely stunted emotional development.

> If you have decided that I am to stay here, don't bother to write ever again. Don't plan on having anything to do with me again. I will no longer consider you my parents and, when I can get home, I will legally have my name changed. If I do not get a letter, I will know what you have decided and, since I have much time on my hands, I will think of a plan on how to kill you both,
>
> Respectfully,
Your son
Dave
>
> P.S. I will say that I am quite serious about killing or at least seeing to it that you are neatly done away with. Your decision. If I stay, I will go through with it. If you do not make me stay, I shall put these thoughts out of my head.

When the parents of the 15 year old writer of this letter received the foregoing communication, they were panic stricken. Quite reasonably they felt that they had a blood-thirsty murderer in their family. When this adolescent boy was initially confronted with what he had written, he genuinely seemed to have forgotten that he had composed this letter several days previously but then, with a happy sigh of recollection, said "Sure I wrote it, sure I meant it at that time. Everyone writes letters like that but you go hunting with your Dad the next day. What's all the fuss?" Such a reaction and response seems almost incomprehensible and outwardly psychotic when seen

166

in a 15 year old teenager if the message is read at a 15 year old level; if this communication is considered at his level of emotional development which was that of a five year old little boy, it was indeed a "normal" five year old proclamation. The incongruity between the emotional immaturity and the physical age level of this teenager made his actions and his statements appear bizarre and outwardly almost psychotic.

When these teenagers were young children, they did not have the intellectual and physical capability to act on these infantile feelings. However, as adolescents they have the physical potential for specific action. When such childlike impulses are expressed in aggressive, sexual, or narcissistic behavior the social results may be catastrophic for the teenager, his family, and his community. In an infantile rage, such an immature teenager may brutally beat someone who thwarts his wishes. In childish frustrations, such an immature adolescent may act on his frankly murderous impulses. With infantile greed, the emotionally arrested teenager may rape and seduce to fulfill his childish cravings. Such antisocial behavior is not due to a defective conscience structure because these teenagers have not developed the emotional capability of having a conscience. Such behavior is not psychotic since these young men and young women do indeed know reality and have a secure concept of their own identity in society. Their behavior is, however, so infantile and so immature that they are profoundly handicapped emotionally and are a potential menace to themselves and their community.

RELATIONSHIP ABILITY

The emotional reactions of these adolescent patients are more readily understood when we consider these teenagers as showing an arrest in personality development. This emotional stunting is best illustrated and most easily diagnosed when the relationship capacity of these young men and young women is evaluated (Greenson, 1954; Brody, 1960; Gedo, 1966). Their limited potential for relating resembles closely the various

167

growth stages in relationship ability seen as the young child grows and develops. This group of disturbed adolescent patients has progressed in relationship ability only beyond the most primitive infantile autistic level of relating to the stage where the young infant relates to part objects or to preambivalent objects but not to the emotional level of mature, ambivalently based interpersonal relationships.

As the normal, growing infant dimly becomes aware of objects outside himself, he reacts first to the feeding breast or to the bottle. Such a bottle can be held by any person, male or female, old or young; the breast can belong to any woman, providing that it is flowing and gratifying. At this normal primitive relationship stage, the infant relates only to part objects—parts that may be attached to any whole. The disturbed adolescent, with the most severe emotional developmental arrest, may be limited in his personality development to such a very simple relationship capability, where he relates only to people for what they can give but where this giving could realistically be performed by any person. People who work and who live with such immature teenagers may feel "used" and "taken advantage of," a feeling which may well be justified. However, such adolescents are unable to relate at any more meaningful levels than to use people solely as part objects.

> After two years on the unit, we find he takes us for what he can get. If he can use us to play pool, he will be nice to us until the game is over. If you are taking people swimming, he will tag along as nice as could be until the swimming is over—then you do not exist anymore.

Such adolescent behavior can conceivably produce an enraged environmental response. To the disturbed adolescents whom we are now considering, this infuriated environmental reaction is totally beyond comprehension insofar as they do not have the emotional capacity to appreciate that people are more than part objects. These disturbed teenagers are not deliberately "using" people; rather they lack the emotional ability to see others as whole people. These young men and young

168

women can only relate to the human beings around them as to a collection of part objects, as hands that can bake a cake, as a mouth that can scream, as a foot that can play soccer. These teenagers do not have the emotional ability to see people as meaningful whole human beings, people with feelings, people with a past, a present, and a future. The total relationship capability of such handicapped teenagers is based solely on immediate experience, completely in the present, totally in response to the giving-taking activity of the moment—nothing beyond, nothing emotionally deeper, nothing more integrated. These childlike adolescents can relate very positively to one ability or to one quality of a staff member and equally strongly but totally negatively to another attribute in the same person immediately afterwards. Such a teenager may respond warmly to the swimming instruction of a nursing aide, only to leave the swimming area and steal the cigarettes from the same aide's jacket pocket without a qualm. To this disturbed adolescent there is no connection between the two actions. He is only capable of dealing with people as part objects—hands and legs that teach swimming as one experience, available cigarettes in an unguarded jacket as another experience with both experiences separate and unconnected and, in the mind of such a teenage patient, to be reacted to separately—based only on the immediate need of that moment.

These teenagers at this very limited stage of emotional development are not capable of trusting or of being trusted. They lack the emotional ability which is required to invest in people as permanent, dependable objects. They do not deliberately deceive but rather they are unable to integrate meaningful experiences and long-term goals. These teenagers resemble the "Juvenile Imposter" described by Aichhorn (1964). They are indeed imposters in that, superficially, they may give the appearance of trusting and being trustworthy. These adolescents are of normal intelligence, physically capable, and appreciative of reality—yet, in their relationship ability, they can see other human beings merely as unintegrated parts and functions. Since these disturbed adolescents at this primitive stage of emotional development live totally in their immediate experience, they lack the basic ability to plan. They cannot delay immediate pleasure for long-term goals since they do not have the emotional capability for pleasurable anticipation (Engel, 1960). Whatever pleasure and whatever gratification they do not experience in the immediate present, they do not expect ever to receive because these adolescents have no integrated concept of a future. They are realistically puzzled and most bewildered by any suggestion of future rewards for present delay. They feel understandably resentful and cheated if they are asked to postpone gratification, even by someone they like (Rinsley, 1965).

At a slightly more advanced stage of normal emotional development, as the infant grows, he gradually begins to see the breast as belonging to a consistent mothering person. The normal infant starts to react emotionally not only to the breast but also to a mother, to the mother as a whole object. At this level of personality development, the growing infant reacts to this external object as to something all good or all bad. The infant cannot tolerate bad and good feelings about the same object without disrupting anxiety. When faced with an angry anxious, mothering person, the normal infant will show total emotional disintegration. Certain disturbed adolescents, with emotional developmental arrest, relate solely at the primitive relationship stage where their world is divided into the good people and the bad people, totally good or totally bad—those "for me" and those "against me." This dividing line is sharp and absolute; the good, who tend to be a small minority, are absolutely good and absolutely acceptable to this adolescent; the bad are seen as completely unacceptable and completely malevolent. To suggest to such an emotionally limited teenager that a good person might have bad qualities is to propose something unreasonable, impossible and unthinkable. To imply to this immature teenager that a bad person may have good qualities would be considered by him to be just plain stupid or deliberately deceitful. When an immature adolescent functions at this relationship level, he just cannot comprehend the concept that all people have both good and bad qualities and that it is possible to relate meaningfully to someone in an ambivalent relationship. At this preambivalent stage of emotional development, the young man or the young woman splits people in his environment in this all-good or all-bad fashion. Frequently he may give the appearance of playing one person against the other, consciously and deliberately.

> He gives John the credit for everything. It is "Yes John," "Thank you John." Anyone else he never looks at! I doubt if he would spit on me, far less thank me for anything. He treats me like dirt, just dirt—but John can't do anything wrong!

In such a situation as described in this nurse's note, treating team members who do not have a clear clinical awareness of the teenager's very limited relationship capability, might become extremely angry with the adolescent and with each other, under the erroneous impression that the adolescent's preambivalent pattern of relating indicated that the patient or the staff members were playing favorites. Such preambivalent interaction is found in all the adolescent's relationships with each member of his peer group and the therapeutic team. If the disturbed adolescent is involved in a psychotherapy process, most often the psychotherapist is seen by this adolescent as the "all good" person where most everyone else in the therapeutic staff is "all bad." The other treatment staff members may become angry in face of the constant suggestion from the teenage patient that, in this instance, his psychotherapist is all wise, all kind and all giving, whereas everyone else on the therapeutic team, in spite of all their efforts, is seen as "dirt" in the eyes of the adolescent patient. In such a treatment situation, staff resentments tend to arise and may react against optimum treatment if the treating personnel are unaware that the different relationships they have with the teenage patient represent this adolescent's maximum ability to relate. The patient-team interaction is in no way due to staff favoritism nor is it a deliberate attempt at team splitting by the teenage patient.

As Fairbairn (1952) suggests, these relationships at this pre-ambivalent level are the basis of the first primitive identification. The grossly disturbed teenager, whose ego has developed only to this very limited relationship stage where emotional objects are either all good or all bad, does begin to identify with the all-good person or the all-bad person with whom he has a significant relationship. The reality that he does see these meaningful people without mixed feelings makes it much easier for him to establish this very primitive form of identification, an identification process that is of course largely based on the teenager's own emotional projections.

During the next normal stage in natural emotional growth, the developing infant should grow in his relationship ability to the point where he can see meaningful people ambivalently, as human beings with both good and bad features. The growing child discovers that people are not perfect and, in so learning, he finds that he himself does not have to be perfect to be loved, to be accepted and to be successful. When the child or the adolescent can tolerate ambivalent relationships and can view himself ambivalently, he can then fully identify with meaningful human beings, meaningfully good or meaningfully bad, meaningfully strong or meaningfully weak, meaningfully masculine or meaningfully feminine. In a treatment process, when the disturbed adolescent has grown emotionally to this stage of personality development when he relates significantly at an ambivalent level, the teenager usually does not require inpatient treatment and can be helped better on an outpatient basis. If it is shown during an evaluation process that the conflicted teenager does have this ability to relate at an ambivalent level and has sufficient emotional strength to deal with the conflicts aroused by ambivalent relationships, it is most likely that he will not benefit from the treatment supports of an inpatient setting but will be more productively helped in some other therapeutic environment.

THE QUALITY OF RELATING

Until these disturbed immature adolescents develop the personal sensitivity to other people that finally comes with ambivalent relating, the quality of their emotional responsiveness tends to be comparatively uncontrolled and unmodified. Their expression of feeling and of impulse, without the modulating effect of ambivalence, is direct, blunt, and primitive. Insensitive, raw emotions can be expressed and acted out without personal anxiety. Hate and anger can be displayed as murderous rage, love as the open wish for absolute total possession. The adolescent with a marked arrested ego development may blurt out, in his anger at some slight or rejection, that he feels like killing. Outwardly such behavior appears psychotic or grossly psychopathic; when the pronounced emotional immaturity of these disturbed teenagers is appreciated, this form of expression can be seen as an outward representation of his inner primitive emotional level. Such grossly immature adolescents will openly and without anxiety proclaim their plans for the sexual conquest of someone whom they say they "love." Frequently, in the most direct fashion they will tell the truth, but this is truth without personal responsibility. In the fashion of a two or three year old, the adolescent patient will openly admit his antisocial behavior and then be most perturbed because this admission does not bring immediate forgiveness and freedom. They protest that they have told the truth so why should they not be permitted to continue to do whatever they wish. These emotionally inadequate adolescents act as if in reality they can "kiss and make it better" like the very young child.

With their very primitive level of emotional understanding, these disturbed teenagers feel no personal qualms about imposing equally primitive demands on other people. When a 15 year old young man with severe developmental arrest was questioned about rumors of his sexual activities with his girlfriend, he emphatically demanded of the staff to: "Ask her if I screwed her. She will tell the truth." He is totally unable to appreciate that such a question might be extremely embarrassing to a young adolescent girl. The teenager feels that his girl-friend is just being asked a fact and should have no difficulty about giving an unemotional answer. An adolescent with profound developmental arrest does not have the emotional capability to appreciate that other human beings can have mixed emotional feelings.

Often these disturbed teenagers simply cannot tolerate ambivalent feelings concerning a meaningful person. They will so exclude one side of a relationship that they appear totally unreasonable or even psychotic. Those people whom they have come to regard as "friends" are held to be totally dependable, absolutely trustworthy, and all loving—in spite of repeated blatant deceit and open rejection. No matter what their "enemies" do, they are considered consistently evil even though there may be frequent instances of demonstrated warmth and obvious caring, which the rational adolescent could not realistically deny but which the markedly immature teenager has to blot out of awareness. When the disturbed adolescent grows emotionally in his natural development or in a treatment process to the growth level where he is able to feel ambivalent relationships, he is then faced with inner stresses caused by these conflictual relationships. Teenagers who do develop emotionally to this level of relating, may regress again to preambivalent patterns of interacting in the face of anxiety-arousing conflicts produced by ambivalence. At a preambivalent emotional level, the adolescent boy can maintain his concept of "good girls" and "bad girls," i.e., good girls to like and to respect, bad girls to use sexually for a kind of intravaginal masturbation. When the adolescent boy matures emotionally to the stage where he can experience meaningful ambivalent relationships about the same girl, he then starts to feel anxiety and inner conflict where he finds himself caring for a bad girl or where he becomes annoyed at a good girl. Frequently the teenage patient will say openly that he cannot permit himself to have mixed feelings lest one type of emotion destroy the other meaningful relationship. He cannot allow himself to care for someone he hates, lest in some way his caring overpowers his hatred and he is left not knowing what to do. He cannot allow himself to get angry at someone for whom he cares, lest his anger destroy what is good and he is left in an emotional vacuum. The personal anxieties aroused by ambivalent conflictual feelings are most painful and at times almost unbearable in teenagers whose ego development is limited.

> Three dollars and nine cents! Jesus Christ! I only had four dollars. Three dollars and nine cents blown on a hotel room—and I feel so ashamed! I got her into bed. She lay there looking at the ceiling. I could see her face reflected in the window above the door. The room was filthy—man, I'm sure I heard bugs creeping on the floor. And do you know, she smelled of B.O. I couldn't even get a head of steam. Whenever I looked at her, I felt like vomiting. I must be getting soft. A year ago, I could have gone to town all night in her. I couldn't do it! I felt dirty. So I told her I was going downstairs to get a fifth. I put on my clothes, went downstairs and ran down the fire escape from the second floor. And I don't even have a dollar left!

In this vivid fashion, a 17 year. old young man describes the conflictual anxieties and the physical tensions he experienced when he tried to have sexual relations with a young eager prostitute. A year previously, when he related only at a preambivalent level, he could have seen this girl as all bad or merely as a vagina, and sensually he could have enjoyed a sustained rape session without any emotional struggle. However, with emotional maturation where he now related to people at an ambivalent level, he saw her as a young woman, dirty but pathetic, someone for whom he now had sympathy as well as exploitative sexual feelings. The reality of personality growth brought with it, as it does with all these emotional retarded adolescents, a new and painful experience of ego anxiety. If these new conflictual tensions are too strong, the ensuing emotional anxiety may cause the adolescent to regress either temporarily to augment his ego strength or permanently where he does not have further growth capability.

THERAPEUTIC APPROACH

The treatment for the adolescent with severe emotional developmental arrest must be firmly based on a sound clinical understanding of the underlying etiological factors, on a clear diagnostic appraisal of the teenager's emotional strengths and relationship capabilities, and on a knowledge of the factors in the teenager's life which tend to perpetuate or to accentuate his illness. As with all other adolescent patients, the first essential step in a meaningful treatment program is to make the teenager's behavior his own responsibility. All too frequently with these adolescents, the treating staff tend to be intimidated by the adolescent threat of infantile tantrums, just as the teenager's parents and peers were intimidated. As long as such blackmail can control the environment for the teenager, he is under no pressure to change—meaningful, growth-producing treatment cannot begin.

These disturbed adolescents have gone through their life, until the time of their hospital admission, controlling and manipulating their environment and those around them, by the most infantile threats and challenges. If the immature adolescent is to grow to age-appropriate maturity, his infantile behavior has to become unrewarding and ungratifying. The childlike teenager needs to learn that his illness, his infantile pattern of relating and self-expression, does not in reality control the world. While such infantile omnipotence is indeed gratifyingly pleasurable to the childlike adolescent, such omnipotence also keeps him isolated and rejected. While it is most personally rewarding to the disturbed teenager to feel that, by threats of tantrums, he can control those around him, it is also nightmarishly frightening to him to feel that his fragile strengths represent the maximum available level of control. He lives in a situation where there is no secure control for his feelings, impulses, and anxieties. He has no safe refuge from anxiety and no lasting protection from his uncontrollable tensions and drives. Too often, the treatment team do not appre-

176

ciate just how frightening it is for any adolescent or for any child to feel that he is beyond control.

If the disturbed adolescent is to grow emotionally, he must begin to trust those around him and himself. Where he controls his environment through his infantile rages and childish threats, he has also made it untrustworthy. Many meaningful adults around him, rather than upset this disturbing adolescent, have tended to surrender to him and thus have helped set up a phoney reality dictated by his childlike menacing. The infantile adolescent often reaches the situation where he is never told the real truth lest he become upset or offended. He finds that he has so terrified the people around him that they insulate him in a world of pretense, deceit and denial. In this unreal world which he has manufactured, the infantile, inadequate adolescent can never realistically trust and, never trusting, he cannot grow in self-confidence and in relationship ability. In the treatment environment, this vicious circle where the adolescent with severe ego developmental arrest, terrorizes his environment by childlike threats, and, in doing so, makes everyone and everything untrustworthy, must be stopped so that the adolescent can start to grow emotionally.

With tears openly running down his cheeks, the six foot, 180-pound 15 year old young man related:

> I never knew what to depend on with my folks. They always say what they think I want and then they do something different behind my back. They make me so mad, I could smash them. I told my old man that— and now he always does what he thinks I want. He is a stupid chicken shit. I won't ever hit them—I don't need to. They always do what they think I want and then they pretend they do it because they decided that way anyhow. Who do they think they are fooling? They do it because I say so and I hate their guts for doing it.

In this kind of family interaction, mutually destructive angers between the parents and the disturbed adolescent often dictate events. These infantile adolescents easily make caring people furious with them. This anger can be readily expressed by allowing the teenager to do exactly what he says he

177

wants—so that people can then watch him destroy himself. Because these parents have been made to feel weak and powerless by their children, they tend to lash out at them in frustrated, barely concealed hatred. Because such adolescents desperately require control and environmental stability, they are overwhelmed by the uncertainty around them and will consequently attack, again and again, those whom they have undermined. As they respond to the demands of their emotionally infantile teenage child, these parents will frequently express their expectation and their hopes that their teenager in some way will be destroyed. As one mother said when she took her daughter home against the recommendation of the hospital staff and against her own wishes.

> She knows we think she should stay in hospital. She will just get into trouble at home. She is going to become a prostitute or get herself killed.

Within 14 months, this 17 year old girl was an active professional prostitute; she has continued in this profession.

In a meaningful integrated treatment program, these adolescent patients need to learn over a period of months and years that, if they act in a childlike fashion, they will be treated exactly as children. If they behave as if they were infants, they will be given the limited responsibilities and minimal privileges of an infant. If they threaten to erupt emotionally, all necessary external controls will be provided; no one will be intimidated and the disturbing teenager will be given as much environmental support as he needs.

The 17 year old young man snarls to the child-care worker:

> Goddamn, you son-of-a-bitch; if you don't let me out of this place, I'll cram your teeth down your throat!
> [The response is as follows:] O.K. John, we know you are scared, we know you are cornered, but this is it. I am not going to let you hurt me, I am not going to let anyone hurt you. If you feel you cannot control yourself, I will get all the staff members necessary to help control you. Just say how many you will need—five, six, eight—as many as necessary. If you are getting so tense and so worried that it is unbearable, we can

give you some medication to make things easier—but no one is going to take threats like these. You are in a mess, you are in a jam, you do not know what to do. Pushing my teeth down my throat just will not be allowed; it will not help you, it will not help me and it will not help anything. We must help you find a better way. It must really be frightening to feel that you can explode in this fashion. For a teenager, this is pretty rough.

Very early in the ongoing treatment process, the infantile adolescent needs to know the emotional security that his childlike patterns of behavior are no longer frightening to those around him. He must learn that there are firm, warm, secure people who can control his illness without hurting and without having to take him over and "run" him. These teenage patients will have to test repeatedly to discover whether the treatment personnel are indeed personally secure and stable and whether they can be trusted. When infantile behavior no longer brings the rewards of omnipotence, such behavior becomes much less acceptable to the adolescent. Over and over again, the talion rule that infantile behavior beings only infantile responsibility and infantile rewards needs to be experienced in the teenager's day-to-day living. As he learns that he cannot control his world and, even more important, that he does not need to control his world in an infantile omnipotent fashion, he concomitantly gets to know that rewards are given only for mature and responsible behavior—behavior which hopefully he himself will find of increasing personal satisfaction.

A favorite testing device used by the markedly childlike adolescent is the waiting game. This is very similar to the young child's threat "I will hold my breath and die and you will be sorry." The emotionally retarded adolescent threatens to do nothing unless his demands are met. In the treatment process, the teenager with severe ego developmental lag, must learn that treatment personnel have, above all else, time to use in the treatment process—they are in no hurry and they can wait much longer than the adolescent can wait. The childish patient learns that as long as he functions at an infantile level, this is exactly the level at which he will be treated—and this environmental response can be maintained indefinitely. If the infantile adolescent is unable or unwilling to grow emotionally beyond his very primitive infantile level, after a suitable trial of growth-oriented treatment, he may be transferred to a more supportive environment where his infantile pattern of relating can be accepted for an extended period, for life is necessary. If the disturbed adolescent does not have the capability of functioning at more than an infantile level, this reality must be faced and considered with the teenager, his family, and with the community. These patients, who continue at a very infantile level of functioning, may have to be maintained in a protected environment for the rest of their lives, for their own care and for the security of others.

There is a special diagnostic group of disturbed infantile adolescents who, though they outwardly trumpet their unwillingness to change emotionally, in reality do not have the ego capability to mature and to develop. These adolescents can be considered diagnostically as functioning at a level between the grossly infantile and the psychotic teenager. These young men and young women give the outward appearance of relating to external objects but, on closer examination, their interactions are seen as solely "reacting against." They never make their own decisions but rather they react against environmental decisions. Outwardly this behavior may be presented as fighting "them," the treating staff, or "City Hall." In actuality, these more disturbed adolescents never have to consider or to form their own opinion as they merely mirror negatively whatever is around them. These teenagers have relatively little individual ego strength but present rather the diagnostic picture of a mirror-ego—whatever personal strengths they seem to possess are only negative reflections of environmental strengths and reactions. Where the treating staff see the disturbed childlike adolescent showing a continued pattern of reacting against, this teenager must be closely evaluated to demonstrate his emotional strengths and capabilities.

The disturbed adolescents with the weakest and most infantile personalities fall very easily into this "reacting against" pattern which may become totally egosyntonic for them—in the treatment setting these inadequate adolescents may learn a sick character pattern. If the disturbed teenager uses this defense pattern of reacting against in a pervasive fashion, his emotional growth may become increasingly stunted and he may show regression of ego growth already present. The disturbed adolescent, with a poorly integrated ego status, who allows himself to fall into this personality pattern of merely "reacting against," may become so permanently weakened emotionally that he is unable to exist outside of an institution; he may need this permanent institutionalization to give him a structure to react against so that he can continue to function. With certain more disturbed teenagers, it may be therapeutically impossible to prevent the development of this mirror-ego because these teenagers lack inherent ego strength. When they are dealing with other infantile adolescents who do possess sufficient personality strength to grow emotionally, the therapeutic staff must very seriously consider whether they should disrupt environmental patterns which support and perpetuate a reacting against character structure. With such an adolescent it might be helpful to lower his level of inner anxiety by the use of medication; with less inner pressure he may be better able to use his limited ego resources to make his own decisions and to form his own opinions. Where the adolescent is tending to become parasitic on his peer group, it might be therapeutically helpful to separate him from this group even though he may become temporarily more anxious and disruptive.

Many disturbed adolescents, who present with emotional developmental arrest, do have the capability of becoming socially acceptable citizens within the continuum of emotional normality. Once these teenagers start to gain pleasure from mastery and from ego growth, they may show very rapid emotional maturation and development. When they learn that they really can trust themselves and can trust those around them, they may start to grow rapidly in relationship ability. As these teenagers begin to appreciate the growth gratifications which they have missed, they react by mourning the pleasures that they have never had and never will now receive. Typically in a successful treatment process, the inadequate teenager will mature and come to enjoy adolescence in the fullest sense, just as he is about to become an adult—when he can no longer be an adolescent. He has reason to feel bitter over what he has missed but he must appreciate that bitterness is still no excuse for not now going on to full adult responsibility. He should face his realistic sadness and anger but he must mourn his past childhood as past. As an adult he can gain his greatest pleasures in meaningful adult relationships and in personal adult mastery. With a family of his own, he may to some extent be able to enjoy some of the childhood and adolescent experiences he missed in his own growing years, but he can never retrace his steps nor fully compensate for what he has lost.

The treatment program for the adolescent with severe emotional developmental arrest demands perhaps a greater intensity and a deeper treatment investment than the therapeutic process with any other group of disturbed teenagers. The final treatment results may however be of the greatest benefit to the teenager and of maximum gratification to the therapeutic personnel.

Chapter IX

The Disturbed Adolescent with Severe Conscience Defects

The police gave us a choice. Either they would put him (her) in jail or else we had to take him (her) to a psychiatrist.

The judge (sheriff, mayor) told us to get him (her) out of town. Either we had to place him (her) in a mental hospital (residential treatment center, treatment school) or they would send him (her) away for a long time to a prison (industrial school, reform school).

This is the kind of statement made by parents who feel compelled to bring their delinquent adolescent children to "psychiatric treatment" as one socially acceptable method of dealing with them. Other parents, outwardly sophisticated, interpret the first sign of antisocial behavior in their teenager as an obvious indication of severe emotional disturbance and immediately rush him to a center for some kind of inpatient therapy. Psychiatric care, especially inpatient treatment, is too often equated with punishment in the minds of both delinquent teenagers and some of their parents—thus such care is therapeutically inefficient with these teenagers and their families. Other parents see a course of residential treatment as one sure way of getting their child "off the hook" and away from the social retribution for his behavior—consequently residential treatment has little growth-producing effect on such adolescents. Perhaps too readily in our middle-class oriented society we have tended to equate delinquent, antisocial, or "bad" behavior with emotional illness. Too often the words "adolescent" and "delinquent" coexist in our social language. Before any adolescent is admitted to a treatment unit because of disturbing or delinquent behavior, it must be clearly shown that this behavior is the result and the product of severe and pervasive emotional disturbance and ego inadequacy in the teenager. Hospitalization for any other reason is totally contraindicated.

There are many young men and young women, emotionally very competent, who decide deliberately and consciously to act in an antisocial fashion. They have demonstrated, by virtue of their emotional maturity and their coping ability in other social areas, that they have indeed personality strength and impulse control. They are aware of the normal consequences of their behavior and they are quite able to face their age-appropriate responsibilities for whatever they do. Some adolescents grow up in a basically antisocial environment where delinquent behavior is the socially accepted norm. These delinquent adolescents and their delinquent cultures may require "treatment" but this treatment is better provided by the appropriate legal-social authorities—the therapeutic growth experience that comes with appropriate responsibility, rehabilitation, and retraining.

Some severely disturbed adolescents act in an antisocial or socially unacceptable fashion as one part of their generally disturbed pattern of emotional relating. The presenting symptoms of their underlying emotional disturbance may be some form of delinquent, disruptive, or antisocial behavior. These delinquencies may be precipitated by lack of inner personality strength, by uncontrollable impulses, or by the lack of meaningful relationship ties. For some disturbed adolescents, delinquent behavior provides the only available means of anxiety release. For other sick adolescents, the role of the delinquent gives them their only secure identity and their only means of coping with their environment. Where delinquent behavior is merely one manifestation of a more general emotional illness, psychiatric treatment in an inpatient setting may be required. Though various different patterns of adolescent emotional illness are considered in other chapters of this book, disturbed adolescent behavior will now be considered symptomatically and diagnostically in terms of conscience development where personality stunting or dysfunction leads to delinquent behavior. The treatment for this disturbed behavior is the specific therapeutic procedure needed for the underlying emotional disorder.

THE ADOLESCENT "WITHOUT A CONSCIENCE"

The Adolescent Who Relates Only at a Pre-object Level

The whole behavior of some extremely disturbed teenagers is dictated by an inner emotional pattern of tension build-up and tension release. These very sick adolescents are usually diagnosed as being within the psychotic or the markedly infantile emotional continuum. Their outward behavior is dictated not by feelings for those around them but by emotions and impulses arising totally within the adolescent himself. In this fashion, the psychotic youth will sense a mounting tension arising within him which must be discharged by acting out in an unfeeling, insensitive manner. The activity of these highly disturbed adolescents is based totally on their inner needs at a pre-object level of relationship, where meaningful relationships with other people do not exist and do not modulate their behavior.

These adolescents pose a profound medical-legal problem. In their everyday living they may be very much aware of the immediate realities around them. They do not, however, have the emotional and intellectual capability of understanding the long-term consequences of their acts. At the immediate moment they do know with their limited emotional potential what is right and what is wrong. They may appreciate the prescribed penalties and consequences for their behavior yet still they cannot alter this behavior. Their actions are dictated solely by their inner needs, drives, and impulses in a fashion which is not modified by any personal appreciation of laws or of customs.

In this fashion, a 17 year old schizophrenic boy protested to his ward doctor:

> You shouldn't have asked me what I did. You should know there was nothing else I could do except lie to you. You should have known me better than this. You should not have put me in that corner.

This is a very simple, very direct statement made by this remarkably honest teenager. When this young man was cornered by his doctor and questioned about his recent behavior, the teenager's inner tensions rose rapidly and his mounting anxieties could only be relieved by quick lying and by the immediate avoidance of the anxiety-provoking situation. If this psychotic adolescent had been unable to elude this probing questioning, his inner tensions would have risen to the point where he disrupted in uncontrolled, aggressive, and psychotic behavior—behavior dictated solely by his inner impulses.

These markedly psychotic or severely infantile teenagers will tend to discharge in this abrupt fashion sexual, aggressive, and loving impulses. The quality of their impulse discharge is only partially controlled by whatever limited ego strength they do possess. Where the grossly disturbed adolescent has a limited amount of ego strength or where his inner anxieties are pitched at a moderate level, these inner tensions may be relieved by ravenous eating. The disturbed teenager will stuff himself voraciously as if to satisfy an inner craving, but with little sign of immediate personal enjoyment. Where he is more lacking in personality strength or where his inner tensions cannot be fully handled by eating, the severely ill teenager may relieve his anxieties by indulging in explosive private masturbation activities which may shake his room and reverberate through the building. If the treatment staff note that these pathological behaviors are becoming more frequent and more obvious, they should appreciate that the adolescent must be experiencing increasing anxiety with decreasing coping ability. They must be alerted to the possibility that his impulses may express themselves in even more regressive and uncontrolled eruptions. If the inner tensions of such a teenager continue to mount, he may further disrupt in frantic furious aggressive explosions. Without warning, he may attack brutally almost anyone or anything in sight. In a final effort to maintain some semblance of acceptable control, he may rush suddenly and unpredictably from a closed social setting so that he does not explode in violent assaultive behavior. The final disintegrative stage in this process of impulse dyscontrol is the level of total pervasive disruption.

The behavior of these very sick young men and young women is not dictated by a personal sense of right or of wrong. They may indeed intellectually appreciate what is socially acceptable or unacceptable and what is legally and morally correct, but they lack the emotional integrity to restrain themselves from tension build-up and tension explosion (Blackman, Weiss, and Lamberti, 1963). Their level of behavior is totally directed by the surge of their inner emotions. They have no integrated, internalized rules of behavior which can control or direct their impulses. Though they may consciously wish to relate at a more meaningful continued level, their social behavior is totally based on immediate gratification and on the relief of pain. At this very regressed level of emotional development, these psychotic and immature adolescents are devoid of conscience.

> You shouldn't have trusted me. You know you can't trust me. I will tell the truth when I can, but you know that sometimes I cannot.

In this honest yet pathetic fashion, a 15 year old schizophrenic adolescent girl explained her predicament to a child-care worker. The teenager was being entirely candid in saying that those patients emotionally handicapped like herself, cannot be "trusted." They may be able to tell the truth at that immediate moment if truth is less anxiety provoking—but they do not have

187

the ability to maintain truth in the face of their inner impulses. These severely disturbed patients live totally within the experience of the present moment. They do not have the emotional equipment to conceptualize a meaningful relationship, nor can they perpetuate an interaction based on continued trust. While intellectually these adolescents may have goals and hopes, they cannot maintain any long-term projects in the face of their immediate emotional needs. Such adolescents do not show a conscious deliberately thought-out pattern of antisocial behavior. The delinquencies and the disruptive acts perpetuated by these young men and young women are behavioral patterns over which they have no control.

When these sick teenagers sense that they are about to explode disruptively, they sometimes have the emotional capacity to withdraw in an attempt to avoid creating environmental anxiety. Should they be unable to remove themselves, their explosive impulsive actions result in social anxiety and rejection, a response which further provokes tension and inner anxiety in the adolescent thereby leading to greater antisocial outbursts. In this way, a self-perpetuating cycle of teenage disintegrative behavior is established.

These profoundly disturbed teenagers must be treated at the level of their emotional capabilities and handicaps. In any growth-oriented program they must not be burdened emotionally beyond their capabilities. Such teenagers do not have the emotional ability to benefit from punishment. A punitive approach only causes increased inner anxieties. The treating staff must appreciate that these severely disturbed adolescents cannot be trusted and should not be given the emotional burden of being trusted. The problem of trust might so overtax the emotional capability of such teenagers that this outwardly friendly gesture might produce further regression, withdrawal, and emotional disruption. It is necessary to structure the life of these adolescents over a 24-hour-a-day pattern, both within the treatment unit and at any time that they leave the treatment milieu. Some of these markedly disturbed teenagers who have a minimal amount of ego strength may be able to face the reality that they are subject to explosive inner drives; they may begin to appreciate that they do not have the usual sensitivity in ordinary human relationships. Some very sick teenagers do not have the emotional strength to face even in this very limited fashion the reality of their handicaps. It may be necessary to establish an external conscience for these patients by totally patterning everything they do and by planning for them a permanent sheltered environment where rigid rules will maintain stability and security.

If the inner anxieties of these teenagers can be kept to a bearable level within their emotional capabilities, many will gradually grow toward increasing personality strength and toward a healthier adjustment. To bring their inner tensions to a manageable level, these teenagers who relate at a pre-object state, must be given socially acceptable opportunities for tension release. The teenager may need to get on his bicycle and cycle furiously in any direction for an hour. In his secret hiding place on the hospital grounds, the psychotic adolescent boy may have to be allowed to masturbate privately and violently. The grossly immature teenage girl may have to be supported and permitted to run all the way downtown to the public library. The treatment staff may have to tolerate the spectacle of a severely disturbed adolescent girl gorging herself to the point of vomiting. It is socially preferable that she relieve her tensions by eating rather than by more disintegrative and regressed behavior. Where the inner anxieties of the disturbed adolescent are mounting, a quick aggressive workout on the punching bag or the trampoline may reduce the tensions to a tolerable level. At this stage of very severe emotional illness, the most important therapeutic approach is never to place these disturbed adolescents in a situation where meaningful relations based on realistic object relationships and on inner personal conscience would be expected from them because such expectations are totally beyond their competence and consequently are overwhelming.

THE ADOLESCENT WITH A CONSCIENCE STRUCTURE
BASED ON DISTURBED OBJECT RELATIONSHIPS

A. *The Teenager Who Relates to His Own Feelings Projected Outwards*

At such a primitive relationship level, the disturbed adolescent relates only to the image of his own feelings projected outwards—the person, with whom he is "relating," is not being reacted to in terms of any qualities of that human being, but solely as a personification of the teenager's own feelings projected on to him. In such a relationship, the person to whom the teenager relates is merely an emotional blank screen on whom the adolescent projects his own feelings. At this level of emotional interaction, the disturbed teenager really relates only to his own impulses and to his own feelings but these feelings and impulses are now seen by the adolescent as personified in some emotionally invested object. The person to whom the adolescent relates can thus become the focus for the teenager's own benevolent or malevolent impulses and the disturbed adolescent can justify his behavior in this relationship according to these feelings that are projected (Easson, 1967d).

In the following words, an infantile 17 year old boy berates a new child-care worker who had never even noticed the teenager.

> I knew what he was like the moment I saw him. He just didn't like me. He had it in for me. He has only been here eight hours and he hates my guts and I hate his guts. When I get him alone, I'm going to show him that I mean business!

This adolescent patient, based on his own projected feelings, felt fully justified in planning a vicious attack on the child-care worker. In a similar fashion, the disturbed adolescent can see an outside person as someone totally wonderful, as a projection of only good, warm, positive feelings. Sometimes, when these feelings are erotized and the adolescent patient acts on them, his behavior is likely to become most disruptive socially.

I don't know what came over her. I knew all along that she was in love with me. You can tell it from the way she smiled, from the way she looked and from the way she laughed. But when I tried to kiss her, she raised holy Hell. She hollered and screamed and tried to kick me. I guess I don't understand women.

What this young man did not appreciate was the reality that all along that which he had been perceiving in this girl, was his own projected feelings and hopes. The adolescent had never appreciated the fact that this young woman was very comfortably married and not even remotely interested in him. In fact, her total disinterest may have made her more of an emotionally blank screen and thus more likely to have feelings projected on to her and reacted against. For this reason it is therapeutically essential that treating staff members allow themselves to be emotionally solid real people. It becomes more difficult for obviously human persons to be reduced emotionally to a screen for projected feelings.

Frequently when these disturbed adolescents react against their own perceptions and projections, the people they react against tend to get in the position of acting out these projections. If the disruptive teenager feels that he is being disliked or rejected by those around him, his resultant behavior may produce an active, reality-based rejection and dislike.

When they keep saying to you that you are a son-of-a-bitch, eventually you feel like giving it back to them. I started by liking that guy but he kept needling and nagging at me until finally I did dislike him—the way he said. I hate him for doing this to me and I despise myself for letting him do it.

This was the comment of an angry, bewildered child-care worker who felt sincerely and correctly that he had been pushed into reacting toward an adolescent patient in a fashion which the worker himself did not desire. This teenage boy had projected onto this sensitive worker only angry and aggressive impulses; the adolescent patient had then acted toward the child-care worker, as if the worker indeed were nasty and threatening, so that, eventually, the young patient made himself

191

unbearable to this staff member. The worker then found himself acting back angrily and destructively toward this adolescent who had started off by projecting his own angry and destructive feelings on to the worker. In a similar fashion, when the disturbed patient projects on to a staff member only warm and benevolent feelings, it is very easy for this team member to become all-giving and all-good—it is very pleasant and much easier to be the "nice guy." In this fashion, the disturbed behavior of such limited adolescents who act out against their own projected feelings, tends to become perpetuated; the actions and the feelings of these teenagers become based on concrete reality when the people in their environment start to act out the projected feelings of these adolescents. The environment then becomes part of the patient's illness and reinforces this sick behavior.

As an essential first treatment step in helping such a disturbed adolescent, the whole therapeutic team must be extremely careful that they do not act out the patient's projection. If the young man or the young woman can be dealt with only on the basis of day-to-day reality, the teenager may then have to face the discrepancy between what he feels and thinks he sees and what reality presents repetitiously to him day after day. The caring staff must be very sensitive to the emotional task with which they are facing the disturbed adolescent. Any open discrepancy between his fantasied projections and his intruding reality will cause inner anxiety in the teenage patient. If the adolescent patient has sufficient basic personality strength, this increased anxiety may prompt him to alter his perception and to change his emotional patterns. If however, this increased tension is more than his ego can tolerate, the discomfort will lead to regression, withdrawal, and possibly more overtly psychotic behavior. In the ongoing treatment process with such a disturbed teenager the adolescent must be faced with only as much inner tension as he can handle with his personality resources and with the supports available to him in his treatment environment.

B. Pre-ambivalent Relationships

When the disturbed teenager has the emotional ability to relate only at a pre-ambivalent level, he is capable of having personal feelings for an outside person as a real human being but he sees only the good qualities or the bad qualities of the person to whom he is relating. His behavior toward his environment and the people around him is thus dictated by this all-or-nothing pattern of interacting. He judges people as all good or all bad. Because of his emotional perception, the teenager's behavior toward his environment and the people in his family and culture tends to be totally in one direction or totally in an opposite direction without modulation. He feels and he believes sincerely that he is justified in being completely angry and totally aggressive toward someone whom he considers and thinks he knows to be all bad; in his mind, there are absolutely no modifying and redeeming features about such a person. On the other hand, the disturbed adolescent who relates at this pre-ambivalent level is totally and completely accepting of a person whom he sees as all-good. With his very limited emotional capability to maintain only pre-ambivalently based relationships, such a teenager evolves a form of primitive conscience structure that allows him to act in an abrupt, aggressive, destructive fashion where he believes that the people around him are themselves all bad or all destructive. He feels honestly and sincerely that he is fully justified in his own attacking behavior because he believes that, if he does not act, it is likely that he will be acted against. Since he regards some people as being totally against him, he is thus absolutely justified in his own mind in taking all he can from such people. In the same fashion where he believes that a selected few people are all for him, he feels impelled to be all-giving and all-trusting toward these people; in his sincere belief, these favored few have absolutely no faults and will do him no harm.

It is exceedingly trying for any member of the therapeutic staff to find he is perceived constantly as bad, wicked, untrustworthy, or stupid by a disturbed adolescent for whom that staff member consistently does try to do his very best. Week after week and month after month, the teenager may highlight mercilessly the faults and the errors, the human frailties and the ever-present stupidities in whatever that particular staff person may try to do. Since we all have our inadequacies, the adolescent who relates at this pre-ambivalent level can always focus his pre-ambivalent perception on some realistic human failing. After weeks, months, or even years of being seen only as evil, nasty, or destructive, it is an understandable human reaction to respond in an angry, aggressive fashion to this kind of disturbed adolescent. If the treatment-team members do fall into this therapeutic trap whereby they themselves become totally unrealistic and react back in a pre-ambivalent fashion, the disturbed teenager's pre-ambivalent pattern of relating may become perpetuated and accentuated because his distorted perceptions have been strengthened by the reality of his environment.

Should a staff member be perceived as all-accepting, all-loving and all-good, it is most difficult for this member of the treatment team to frustrate or to refuse gratification to the adoring but sick adolescent. Unless all team members are alerted to this treatment dilemma, a staff member, who is reacted to in this pre-ambivalent fashion as being all-good, may become unrealistically all-giving and all-kind to this disturbed teenager. In this treatment situation there is great pressure and great personal temptation to give the teenager exactly what he says he wants, without really considering whether such constant giving is therapeutic and growth-producing—because this giving perpetuates an outwardly blissful relationship. Many problems of staff identification and counteridentification with the adolescent patients arise in the treatment of these teenagers who have the emotional capacity to relate only at the regressed level of projective and pre-ambivalent relationships (Caplan, 1966; Christ and Wagner, 1966). If the disturbed adolescent is ever to mature in the development of conscience and relationship beyond such primitive stages, he must have in the treatment environment a constant experience of dealing with human beings in realistically ambivalent relationships. He must learn to face the fact that no human relationship is totally benevolent or malevolent. In some fashion he must learn to tolerate with his own strengths or with external supports the natural anxieties aroused by conflictually based relationships.

C. Ambivalent Relationships

If a disruptive adolescent is brought for psychiatric examination and consideration for inpatient treatment, and it is ascertained during the examination process that he has the emotional ability to relate at an ambivalent level, it is unlikely that he will require admission to a residential treatment center. A teenager with this high level of relationship capability and inherent ego strength usually has the basic emotional capacity to use a less supportive, less directive environment. In the course of productive residential treatment, many disturbed adolescents will grow and mature until they reach the emotional level where they can maintain ambivalent relationships. When such a teenager is able to relate to people as human beings with both good and bad qualities, he can now begin to accept himself with his own capabilities and his own handicaps. No longer does he need to see himself as all-good or all-bad, but rather he can begin to face the reality that, like every human being, he does have individual strengths and he does have personal limitations. When the disturbed teenager has matured to such an advanced relationship level, he is now able to form reality-based meaningful identifications, identifications founded on the feelings and the reactions of real human beings around him. As he relates at this more integrated emotional level, the maturing adolescent starts to internalize and to stabilize for himself a definite sensitive conscience. At this integrative stage in the treatment process, the therapeutic personnel must be especially clear as to the standards and the expectations they transmit to this maturing teenager. This is the time when the caring staff must be totally sincere in the guidelines and the examples they offer to the adolescent.

When the teenage patient related at a more primitive, non-ambivalent level, his behavior was dictated only by the strength and the quality of his own inner feelings and impulses. When he has matured to' the point where he identifies realistically with human beings, he can internalize and integrate in his conscience and his ego development both their positive and their negative expectations. In the developing treatment process, the therapeutic team now have the task of helping the growing young man or young woman to form a final stable conscience structure. These maturing teenagers are extremely sensitive to each communication they are given by meaningful people in the environment (Johnson, 1949). If the caring staff tell these teenagers that they are ready to take responsibility, yet somehow never give them this responsibility, the emancipating adolescent readily gets the message that irresponsibility is really what is expected and in some way will be rewarded. If the treatment goal is to help the teenager to evolve his own personal, responsible conscience with a due sensitivity to the duties of the young adult but yet the teenager is never given the burden and the growth task of dealing with these responsibilities, he will be unable to build a strong conscience. The young patient needs to face and to handle the burdens of responsibility before he can finally establish an adult conscience structure.

If staff members loudly proclaim one pattern of behavior as being acceptable but still suggest another as being perhaps easier, this staff expectation of irresponsibility is quickly and clearly communicated to the adolescent.

After a 15-minute dissertation on the evils of promiscuity and premarital sexual relationships, a naturally warm, paternal child-care worker undermined his conscious message by ending: "It is wrong to use a girl sexually, but, if you have to, make sure you wear a condom."

When an immature 15 year old girl was caught stealing from a local supermarket, she was lectured at length by a staff member about her "stupidity." Eventually the young girl stopped the team member with the comment: "What you are really saying is 'Do not steal but if you do, make sure you are not caught.' "

As these maturing adolescents move finally into general society and stabilize their own personal conscience structure, the example of the treatment team must be loud, clear, and unambivalently positive. Many of these disturbed adolescents have come from families where antisocial behavior was supported and approved in some fashion (Carek, Hendrickson, and Holmes, 1961). As they grow toward a healthier adaptation, they must be able to give up these old negative identification figures and use healthier meaningful relationships around them for solid conscience formation. If the adolescent is to undergo this kind of conscience transformation and maturation, he is forced to live through an emotional transition stage when he has given up his old conscience patterns but has not yet fully incorporated new structures. During this growth-transition period, the teenager is especially vulnerable to environmental example, direction, and approval. At this stage of his progress toward health and conscience formation, the treatment team must be most clear in their standards and expectations (Goldsmith, 1963). Once the adolescent himself has developed a definite, secure conscience structure based on reality and on warm positive relationships, he can then become realistically flexible. It is the emotional task of the adolescent to develop this conscience flexibility; the treatment team must remain consistent, certain, and stable.

Treatment of the Adolescent with Conscience Defects

At these various levels of relationship ability and social competence, the adolescent may be considered as having a conscience defect or as being delinquent. Only when this "delinquent" behavior is indeed due to ego defects and to impaired relationship capability should an inpatient treatment process be considered for this teenager. Where the adolescent's emotional disability is so marked that his interactions are at a pre-object, projective, or pre-ambivalent level, inpatient treatment may be the therapeutic program of choice. Where the disturbing adolescent has the more mature emotional capa-

197

bility for reality-based, ambivalently cathected relationships, the kind of help he may require may be better provided in a school, in a legal institution or, if it is considered that he does require psychiatric therapy, in an outpatient treatment program.

Chapter X

The Psychotic Adolescent

When a cohesive, growth-oriented treatment program is being planned for each psychotic adolescent, it is essential first to clarify the type of psychotic reaction manifested, as well as the emotional significance of this psychotic pattern of behavior for the given individual. A treatment approach which does not meet the specific needs of the adolescent psychotic, or a therapeutic plan which is continued after the program has ceased to benefit, may not only be completely useless but may actually cause crippling emotional disruption or personality regression of a permanent nature. The teenager's psychosis may provide him with his one stable identity, his only permanent way of living, and his sole method of coping. It is necessary to ascertain just how long this psychotic state has been present and how fixed is the emotional pattern. The teenager's psychotic method of living may be a totally integrated part of his personality and may form the larger part of his functioning ego. The psychotic state may provide him with a pattern of living that allows him to continue functioning in what would otherwise be an unbearable situation. Thus, in planning a useful treatment program, it is necessary to clarify the relative extent of the teenager's psychotic and nonpsychotic ego strengths.

From the adolescent's family, school, and social history, the depth and the quality of the meaningful relationships which he has been able to maintain over the years can be learned (Pitt and Hage, 1964). With the understanding that can be gained from this background history and from a psychiatric examination, a reasonable, individually oriented treatment program can be established and the probable long-term prognosis delineated. If the disturbed psychotic teenager has shown only a psychotic reaction pattern throughout his life, there is little reasonable chance that he will totally relinquish this psychotic identity during any treatment program which is established in his adolescent years. If, from an early age, he has used an autistic or a psychotic behavioral pattern to cope with his tensions and to develop emotionally, it is extremely unlikely that he will be able to evolve a nonpsychotic personality structure during any adolescent treatment process. If, on the other hand, there are reports of past meaningfully healthy interactions, and if there are indications that the teenage patient's psychotic behavior is a reaction to unbearable stresses posed by meaningful but pain-producing relationships, the prognosis for a stable development of a nonpsychotic ego identity is much more hopeful (Carter, 1942; Freedman and Bender, 1957; Mishler and Waxler, 1966).

In his follow-up study on adolescent inpatients, Warren (1965a) mentions in passing that five of the 25 psychotic teenagers he describes were diagnosed as showing a manic-depressive psychosis. Carter (1942) in his study of adolescent psychoses states that 17 of the 78 young patients whom he discusses were classified as manic-depressive; five of these 17 teenagers were said to have had a "schizophrenic overlay." These relatively high percentage reports of manic-depressive teenagers are not duplicated by other authors. Generally, manic-depressive illness in children and in adolescents is considered so rare that there have been reports of individual cases (Anthony and Scott, 1960; Olsen, 1961). Undoubtedly manic and depressive syndromes do occur with greater frequency than they are diagnosed in adolescent patients, but these emotional illnesses are often missed, not only because the physician does not have such a diagnosis in mind but also because the adolescent typically expresses his affective symptoms in physical activity or in somatic symptomatology. The frenetic pace of the adolescent may be the only outward expression of manic thought processes. Similarly, an automobile accident may be the only way in which the profoundly depressed teenager manifests his deep hopelessness. Parents and teachers may welcome teenage social withdrawal and apathy as a respite from adolescent activity but such behavior, in reality, may be the outward expression of a disabling depression. The physician may treat a wide range of bodily ailments and physical aches without ever comprehending that the teenage patient is somatizing a depressive or a manic illness. Since these manic and depressive teenage patients are rarely seen at this time in an inpatient treatment setting, this chapter on the psychotic adolescent will focus on the schizophrenic teenager.

When a treatment program is being planned for the teenage psychotic, it is often helpful to subdivide such disturbed young patients clinically into those showing "process" or "nuclear" schizophrenia and those who demonstrate a "reactive" schizophrenic process (Kantor and Herron, 1966). These clinical subdivisions are useful in planning the treatment program for the psychotic teenager but are in no way exclusive or absolutely immutable (Higgins, 1964).

Process Psychotic (Nuclear Schizophrenic) Adolescents

The disturbed adolescent, who manifests a process psychotic behavioral pattern, is relatively comfortable with his idiosyncratic and outwardly illogical personality state. His psychotic character patterns are integrated to form a psychotic ego (Kasanin and Kaufman, 1929). For the most part, the process schizophrenic adolescent reacts to the outside world in a psychotic fashion. His methods of coping with his inner drives and with his adolescent emancipation struggles are all so directed and so controlled by his idiosyncratic fashion of thinking that his psychotic ego state and character structure are continually perpetuated, reinforced, and strengthened. His psychotic pattern of living and his psychotic fashion of adjusting

201

to his environment are inner directed but egosyntonic. Most disturbed teenagers, in this process psychotic group, have been psychotic all their lives. These adolescents are the autistic, the symbiotic and the schizophrenic children now grown to adolescence. They are the psychotic adolescents in the psychotic family. These disturbed adolescents are the future adult simple schizophrenic patients. Psychosis has become for them a life style, an integrated pattern of behavior, and the way of their continued emotional growth.

THE AUTISTIC CHILD GROWN INTO ADOLESCENCE

Bill was described by his parents as living in a "world of his own." As an infant he was always very quiet and tended to play by himself. For hours at a time, he would lie smoothing the silken texture of his bedcover. Even before he went to grade school, he spent most of his time alone, playing with clock mechanisms. In primary school, he appeared absolutely disinterested in other children and, though he had an excellent mathematical ability, he consistently failed in all his school subjects including mathematics. He seemed to have no personal interest in the usual academic learning. Since he was not socially disruptive in the classroom setting, he was passed from one grade to the other as he grew older, even though he was failing scholastically.

When Bill grew into puberty, he seemed to become more withdrawn and even more preoccupied with clock mechanisms. He would spend long evening hours working and reworking intricate clock plans. In high school, he was completely isolated socially and his insensitive behavior caused increasing tension and rejection amongst his peers. Eventually when, totally oblivious to everyone around him, he walked right through the color guard during the Presidential funeral ceremonies at his local school, his action caused so much community indignation that a psychiatric examination was forced on the family. At the time of this evaluation Bill, now 14 years old, lived in a world populated only by clocks and by clock mechanisms. Everything around him he saw in terms of time, clock wheels, and clock hands. In his mind, relationships were evaluated according to minutes of involvement. Rewards were meaningful to him only when they brought more clocks.

Since early infancy, this adolescent boy had lived in a psychotic world and had evolved an almost totally psychotic ego structure. He himself was comfortable with his psychotic pattern of behavior and felt pain and anxiety only when those around him reacted angrily or anxiously to his idiosyncratic behavior. He had absolutely no personal motivation to change his character state. Indeed, he did not possess sufficient healthy, reality-based ego strengths to allow him to contemplate at any level any change in his psychotic behavior. His psychotic form of adaptation constituted almost all the personality strength he possessed. The most beneficial treatment for this young man, and for similar nuclear schizophrenics is to help them live with their autism in the wider nonautistic world.

THE SCHIZOPHRENIC CHILD GROWN TO ADOLESCENCE

Certain psychotic children grow up constantly relating to their external environment but in a bizarre fashion. Their relationships are emotionally meaningful to them but are psychotically based, thereby perpetuating and strengthening their psychotic ego states. Unlike the withdrawn autistic child, the schizophrenic adolescent lives in and relates to his environment but the quality of his relationships and the emotional gratification he gains from such interactions are idiosyncratic and psychotic in nature.

John was deliberately conceived by his parents in a conscious attempt to hold the parental marriage together. His mother was addicted to barbiturates even before he was born, while his father, a successful business man, had little time or energy for his wife and his children.

John was described by both parents as having been a precocious infant and a child "always into things." Even as a very young child, his activity was difficult to control and he appeared to be hypersensitive to the feelings of those around him. When he was two years old, his only sibling, a brother, was born; John's furious screaming and jealous tantrums kept his house in an uproar thereafter. From that time on, he began his pattern of setting fires, stealing, sadistically killing animals, and disrupting the neighborhood whenever he could. From an early age, he was described by people outside the family as a "loner" and a "weirdo." His insensitive, erratic, impulsive behavior at school alienated and frightened his schoolmates. His academic work was totally unpredictable; at times his performance was almost brilliant, on other occasions he failed abysmally in the most simple tasks.

Periodically, psychiatric treatment was recommended, started, and discontinued because John's parents felt that such treatment either did him no good or made his behavior worse. The family built a high wall around the house garden to keep John in but this containment wall merely provided a challenge rather than a control. When John was 13 years old, he set a neighbor's home on fire, ostensibly because he did not like the color of the newly painted house. This time, at the insistence of the local police, John was again examined psychiatrically.

He was an intelligent, verbal boy who expressed absolutely no personal anxiety over his continued pattern of stealing, fire setting, and destructiveness when he did not get his way or when he wanted attention. He was very open about his pleasure and delight over the anxiety, the confusion, and the anger of his family and his neighbors about his behavior. Whenever the question of his responsibility for his actions was raised, John reacted blandly by stating that "everyone is against me." Long-term hospitalization was recommended for this young man but, shortly after he was admitted to the hospital, John wrote home in the following vein—

Dear Mother and Father:

I have just come out of therapy. Enclosed is another report I did for class. For the past two weeks I have been staying up until 12:30 watching T.V. I'll probably fall asleep in class the next day but who cares. Lately I have been getting F's in arithmetic. It is fun to get an F because the teacher gets all upset. My English teacher is a little shrimp. That's what I call her. Someday I'm going to kill her. Now I think I'll go and turn on some water faucets or hide my roommate's camera. Take lousy care of yourself and go walk across the Kennedy Freeway or something.

Love,
John

P.S. What I need now is a King snake. If anything new happens, you will be the first to hear. Your loving son who wants to get into the F. State Hospital.

John.

This 13 year old adolescent boy had no qualms at all about his disruptive, crazy behavior. His sole source of emotional gratification came from the attention that such psychotic behavior brought. When he was unable to act out disruptively, he did not know what to do with himself insofar as this kind of behavior had become his total ego, his sole method of functioning. The only identity this young man had was that of being "crazy." If, by some means, this psychotic identity could have been removed, John would have found himself with no ego strength and no defenses. As he himself said "Look Doc, if I stopped acting this way, I'd be a nothing, just a nothing."

THE FUTURE ADULT SIMPLE SCHIZOPHRENIC

Frequently it is said about patients who in adult life will be diagnosed as simple schizophrenic that they had gone "unnoticed" as they grew or that they have had a chameleonlike quality. These patients, in adolescence, cover over their basic lack of ego strength by mirroring the actions and the feelings of those around them, by copying their peers. When they are unable to mirror or to imitate, they then withdraw or surrender emotionally. If withdrawal is not possible, they may be faced with such unbearable emptiness and total confusion that a disintegrative panic is not unlikely.

When George was eight years old, he was seen by the local school psychologist because, for no apparent reason, he had been crying frequently in class. At the time of this examination, nothing unusual could be found with the boy and he was described as "a fine child." Since he was an only child, he was his mother's constant companion while his busy father was away from home on long trips. George was described by his parents and by his teachers as consistently quiet and as "no trouble." He had no special friends and few apparent interests. His teachers stated that he was "quiet as a mouse" in grade school. Though he was of superior intelligence his academic performance was usually near the failing mark but, as the examination time approached, routinely his parents would both tutor him for several days so that each time he just passed.

When he reached adolescence, George began to rove with teenage gangs but, usually for reasons not apparent to his parents, he tended to be quickly rejected by these peer groups. His school mates described him as a "creep" and a "drag." He was said to be "no fun." His school work began to deteriorate even further and no amount of tutoring seemed to make any difference. As his parents and his teachers said, George did not seem to be able to "carry over" the teaching lesson from one day to the next. Though he might appear to understand the lesson one day, by the following day he seemed to have no recollection at all of what he had been taught. He was listless and apathetic when by himself but "quite a different boy in a crowd"—he assumed the identity and the goals of the group he happened to be with at that particular moment. When this teenage boy's crying spells became even more marked and his school work even less acceptable, he was seen in psychiatric examination. This evaluation process revealed a totally disorganized young man with hardly any signs of individual ego capability. When he was faced with his own inadequacies, he could only weep in silent, affectless tears.

The quality of crying shown by this young man is almost diagnostically specific for the process schizophrenic patient. These children and teenagers, when faced with an emotional task beyond their capability, cry silently in a numbed fashion with little outward emotion. Their tears run down a stolid face and drop unheeded on the floor. The adolescent does not appear depressed, angry, or anxious but rather he gives the impression of being emotionally empty.

THE PSYCHOTIC ADOLESCENT IN THE PSYCHOTIC FAMILY

The final clinical example of the process schizophrenic adolescent is the disturbed teenager who is a psychotic member of a psychotic family group. In some families, and in some cultures, psychosis is the natural, normal way of existence. Everyone in this psychotic group functions on a psychotic level so that all emotional growth processes perpetuate and accentuate individual psychotic reactions. To be emotionally healthy and normal would be considered unacceptable in such a family environment.

> Sure we're all nuts. Father is nuts, Mom's nuts, Bill's nuts, Meg's nuts, and even the cat is queer in the head. We like it that way, it's fun!

This realistic statement by a 15 year old young man represents his attempt to explain a visit home where, on the Fourth of July, the whole family became involved in a fire-cracker throwing fight in which several family members were severely burned; for an after-fireworks social entertainment, this outwardly profoundly Catholic Negro family then tried to "crash" a local Ku Klux Klan rally. Finally, to round out the day's celebration, the male members of the family ended up by having a knife-throwing practice session—initially with a tailor's manikin but later with the family cat as a target. The description by this teenage patient that the members of his family were naturally "nuts" was quite accurate since all known family members did appear to be psychotic in varying degrees.

206

Many of these psychotic families live and communicate in a constant crazy metaphor. They perpetuate a "folie à famille." Psychosis pervades all aspects of family living.

In most families, private family jokes represent the essence of family interaction and have a personal, idiosyncratic family significance, usually based on the very individualized sharing at the most meaningful level of family interaction. Family jokes embody the heart of family warmth and relating. The family jokes and the private terms of family endearment in the psychotic family frequently give the essence of this psychotic structure which perpetuates psychosis. Over several years in an inpatient treatment process, a young psychotic adolescent patient was constantly addressed by father in his letters as "Frankie." This repeated mode of greeting was puzzling to the treatment staff since the teenager's name was John. Only very late in the treatment process did the adolescent boy and his father reveal that "Frankie" was short for "Frankenstein" and that the father saw his son as a Frankenstein monster. Each letter of communication over these years of treatment had told the boy very directly that his father expected him to be a grotesque monster.

For months another father and son maintained a lengthy intricate correspondence during which they discussed the Viet Nam war situation. In the casework process and in the boy's psychotherapy, father and son eventually admitted that this letter exchange about the Viet Nam situation was merely the expression of a crazy family metaphor in which they were considering their own relationship. For both the father and his son, the Communists personified their own ambivalent fears of their psychotic impulses. In their letters, they struggled over whether the Communists (their psychosis) should win and take over the country or whether South Viet Nam could take the risk of an untried pattern of democratic government (a healthy adjustment). The South Vietnamese (the healthy reality-oriented ego forces) were repeatedly described in these letters as being weak and untrustworthy—a most realistic appraisal of the emotional strength of this boy and this family. In this continued psychotic metaphor, the "United States advisors" represented the treatment personnel who were both welcomed and hated. It was feared that the South Vietnamese were so weak that the United States advisors would take over the whole country—that the patient's ego resources were so fragile that he might be controlled by outside ego forces in a fashion he both wished and feared. In their correspondence and in their other communications, this father, this son, and this family interacted in their own idiosyncratic, very private, special psychotic way. Only after lengthy intensive treatment process did these family members develop sufficient healthy ego strength to allow them to give up their psychotic patterns of relating in favor of more socially shareable patterns of interaction.

The Treatment of the Process Psychotic Adolescent

A psychotic mode of living has become a permanent, relatively immutable way of life for these teenagers who present with a process psychosis. Their emotional and intellectual energies and capabilities are integrated and sublimated in a crazy fashion that perpetuates and extends their psychotic state. Such psychotic defenses arouse no personal anxiety in these teenagers who feel pain and tension only when the outside world reacts unfavorably and in a pain-producing manner to the idiosyncratic patterns of behavior of these teenagers. When the diagnostic team looks for areas of healthy, nonpsychotic ego strength in these adolescents, such islands of stable functioning may be almost nonexistent, especially in the simple schizophrenic adolescent patient. These process psychotic teenagers are normally intelligent with average physical capability—but they are crazy. They have little or no wish to change their psychotic fashion of adaptation. In point of fact, the treatment team cannot really ask that these adolescents change significantly since, were they to relinquish their psychotic egos, there would be little ego capability left for handling their impulses and anxieties. If the therapeutic team members attempt to remove or to change the psychotic character pattern of interacting shown by these nuclear schizophrenic teenagers, they are then without the means of relating and do not have the basic inherent ego strength to develop new relationship capability.

A 16 year old psychotic boy wrote—

A million trillion people have I killed,
A thousand times have I died.
A thousand men have I loved and many girls
    have I screwed.
All in my mind only.
Oh that this were so.
Better to be a king of evil for at least
    they really have something
Than an emperor of misery
Who has as his councutrives
Hell and loneliness—one in the same.

As this teenage boy so graphically describes in this poem, he has a meaningful identity and a stable purpose (at least in his psychotic process). If by some means his psychotic strengths and his psychotic patterns of relating were removed, he would be faced only with "hell and loneliness." Any treatment process which is directed toward the restructuring of the process schizophrenic's character structure is liable to produce withdrawal, regression, and ego disintegration. In dealing with the process psychotic adolescent, the treatment program must be directed toward helping him live with his psychotic capabilities in a nonpsychotic world.

The process schizophrenic teenager must be accepted at his level of functioning by the entire caring team. The treatment staff cannot change his inherent psychotic ego because this psychotic state is an integral part of the teenager's total personality. In a useful productive treatment process, the adolescent's psychotic strengths can be utilized in the service of his emotional growth. His long-standing psychotic state produces a certain emotional stability and clearly delineated character structure which enables him to cope. Since these adolescents are of normal intelligence, they can be trained to realize that certain

209

patterns of psychotic behavior inevitably bring painful environmental reactions. They can be helped to appreciate that, in many ways, they are profoundly insensitive to their environmental cues. They can be encouraged to face their emotional limitations and, at least partially, to compensate for their continuing personality handicaps. In their constant role as the patient's ally, it is incumbent upon the therapeutic staff to highlight to the process schizophrenic teenager how certain psychotic behaviors inevitably bring unpleasant environmental reactions and how other ways of interacting will cause less rejection or more gratification. This treatment-training must be maintained over an extended period.

> [A considerate child-care worker told a 16 year old psychotic boy with whom he had built up a meaningful relationship over the years:]
> Look Bill, you can think you are Joe Louis and that is your business. But you know and I know that, if you go downtown and tell people that you are Joe Louis, they are liable to lock you up in an unpleasant place for the rest of your life. If you do not want to be locked up, for goodness sake keep your big mouth shut. You can believe what you want to believe but, if you want to go to school, you must live in a certain way—and that means you do not tell people that you are Joe Louis.

In their private discussions with the psychotic patient, the treatment personnel can point out openly and directly those areas of functioning in which there is emotional blindness and insensitivity. These psychotic adolescents must be trained to appreciate and to use verbal and nonverbal cues to compensate for their relative unawareness of the human feelings of people around them. In an almost didactic fashion they can be instructed how to read environmental indications of group and individual feelings. They can be taught how to appreciate the social cues for appropriate behavior and can be conditioned to maintain certain patterns of culturally appropriate behavior as well as to suppress other socially unacceptable reactions. Through repeated instruction and example, they learn to modify their behavior within the social settings that they wish to enter so that they do not suffer personal embarrassment and social pain. This treatment-training process continues in a stable but repetitive fashion over an extended period, in a wide variety of social environments, enabling the adolescent to use his psychotic ego capabilities in a fashion acceptable to both himself and the community.

Where the process psychotic adolescent lacks both the psychotic and nonpsychotic ego capabilities to integrate this kind of training process, the more difficult task of the treatment team is to erect a stable ego shell around him. If he lacks the emotional capability to learn, even in a conditioning fashion, from either painful social experiences or from pleasurable gratification, external environmental structuring and direction may have to be built into everything he does in order that he may continue without disorganization or total autistic withdrawal. In his day-to-day living he can be maintained in the hospital school, in a structured public school setting, or possibly in a very supervised but relatively undemanding boarding-home environment. The simple schizophrenic adolescent who reflects only his environment must be given a secure, permanent environment to reflect. He must be exposed only to supportive situations and to social groups which will provide him with the kind of external ego that will allow him to appear socially appropriate. For a small group of psychotic teenagers who are more limited emotionally, it is impossible either to train them for social adaptability or to build a sufficiently strong external ego structure around them so that they can continue in the community; these patients are then likely to require a sheltered environmental living situation for the rest of their lives.

Consistent long-term milieu therapy is frequently the only treatment required and the only treatment that can be used for most of these process psychotic adolescents. In many instances, an individual, interpretive psychotic process is definitely contraindicated because these process psychotic teenagers cannot tolerate any treatment program which tends to remove their psychotic defenses. In very select instances a regressive-reconstructive treatment process may be contemplated if an unusually experienced psychotherapist can make available five to 10 or more years psychotherapy time. In this treatment situation the psychotherapist would try to establish a meaningful relationship with the psychotic adolescent by first becoming part of his psychotic world so that gradually, over a period of many years, a nonpsychotic pattern of relating can be achieved, based on this treatment bond. The rationale behind this prolonged treatment process is based on a hope that eventually the adolescent will develop a sufficiently solid, healthy, reality-based ego which will enable him to take the profound risk of giving up at least part of his psychotic personality defenses. Frequently in this kind of intensive process, the nuclear schizophrenic patient may regress to a most primitive infantile state in the psychotherapy process and sometimes in the hospital setting as well. This kind of overt primitive regression is extremely disturbing to other patients and to staff members. To undertake such an intensive reconstructive reintegrative process requires a maximum staff integration and investment since many treatment team members become extremely anxious and disturbed at the spectacle of a 16 year old young man or young woman lying in a bed sucking a baby bottle or soiling—and this may be a necessary growth stage if the nuclear schizophrenic patient is to evolve a stable healthy ego status. With consistent integrated hospital support, and intensive, interpretive, rebirth psychotherapy process usually produces only limited treatment results. Even with the most intense, most extensive treatment process, these children tend to remain psychotic, disturbingly antisocial, or cripplingly neurotic. Generally, it appears that by the time they are brought to a treatment process, these adolescents are so stunted emotionally that they have permanently lost the capacity for growth in certain areas of ego capability. The investment of such intensive treatment resources with these patients can only be justified on a research basis.

For the vast majority of nuclear schizophrenic teenagers, milieu therapy is the only required treatment. It may be therapeutically helpful and appropriate to prescribe an individual psychotherapy relationship for the psychotic adolescent who does have some relationship capability; in a supportive, directive teaching role the individual psychotherapist may act as a kind of "super-ally" for the psychotic adolescent. Especially if this teenager is going to move from the residential setting into the larger social community, an understanding supportive psychotherapist may be able to assume some of the directive, strengthening functions of the inpatient treatment team. In order to use this kind of supportive psychotherapy process and to integrate the strength of the psychotherapy relationship as he moves into the community, the psychotic patient must have sufficient ego integrative ability to carry, from one psychotherapy session to the next the direction and the support of the psychotherapy process. Some more limited psychotic teenagers are only able to experience within the immediate moment. They can interact with a psychotherapist in a supporting relationship but they do not have the ability to maintain the teaching-supportive interaction outside the psychotherapy hours. These patients may use the psychotherapist to provide them with concrete direction but they cannot internalize the emotional quality of the relationship. At a more advanced level of emotional development, the psychotic adolescent can integrate the caring-supportive aspects of psychotherapy as a source of ego strength even outside the actual psychotherapy session. If an individual psychotherapy program is prescribed for the process psychotic adolescent, this prescription must be uniquely tailored to his particular needs and capabilities.

THE REACTIVE PSYCHOTIC ADOLESCENT

As the adolescent emancipates from the support and the direction of his family, he is forced to rely on his own ego strengths, on his integrative personality capabilities, and on his relationship capacity. The adolescent separation task forces every teenager to face the reality of his emotional strengths. Where the maturing adolescent has had warm consistent growth-promoting relationships, his teenage personality is liable to be strong, reasonably flexible, and capable. Where his meaningful relationships during his preadolescent years have been inconstant, fragmentary, and painful, his ego integration and his relationship potential are likely to be uncertain and insecure. As the growing teenager separates from his family during the adolescent emancipation process, he relives and re-experiences the past reality of the relationships that have formed his personality and have gone into the development of his capacity for interaction. As he is forced to depend on his own emotional strengths, the developing adolescent experiences once more the deepest meaning of his introjected, internalized parents, family, and friends. Where the relationships in his life have been grossly and painfully ambivalent or malevolent, the teenager is obliged to relive these past anxiety-arousing experiences as he lives through the adolescent separation-emancipation process. When he can only rely on his own self-confidence, he is forced to re-experience, at all levels of emotional feeling, the interactions that originally established his own self-image, his own ego integrity, and his own self-confidence.

Where the growing adolescent has lived through disturbing early relationships, the advent of puberty will confront him with the anxiety-arousing reality that his ego status is insecure and that his relationship capability is poorly established. If these painful and disturbing relationships still continue during his adolescence, the teenager's emancipation task will be doubly difficult. These adolescents find themselves actively reacting to the conflict within their environment and to the struggles and uncertainties within their own personality as they emancipate. If the relationships offered by his family and his peers continue to be painful, uncertain, and anxiety arousing, the adolescent whose earlier relationships may have allowed him to develop only a most uncertain self-confidence and personality integration, may find the emancipation task beyond his ego capability. As his ego anxiety increases and his emotional pain mounts, the anguished teenager may be able to handle this unbearable situation only through a psychotic withdrawal

214

(Warren, 1950). These deeply pained adolescents retreat into an idiosyncratic, autistic world only as a reaction to a situation with which they cannot cope. Although they are able to relate, relationships are so unbearable, that they are forced to withdraw. Unlike the situation with the process psychotic teenager, this withdrawal in the reactive psychotic adolescent is not initially completely egosyntonic or without anxiety (Stein, 1967). These uncertain adolescents would prefer to relate with the outside world if only it were bearable and if only they themselves had the emotional strength to cope with the situation. As Alderton (1963) points out, in this stage of reactive withdrawal the adolescent himself frequently has the ability to observe and to describe the etiological factors and the process of this withdrawal reaction.

> I love my mother but I could kill her. This morning we had a fight. I think it started because I did not want any coffee—I don't know now. At any rate we ended up with her saying "Why don't you go and get yourself shot in Viet Nam"? I could feel it. I could feel the fog coming out of the walls. It crept over me, smothered me. I couldn't see. I couldn't feel. I began to laugh and laugh and laugh. I didn't know why. Just like I'm laughing now. What was I saying?"

In these words, a 16 year old boy described how he was caught in the morass of his mother's loving-destroying hate and his own murderous-caring feelings for her. He could deal with this unbearable emotional conflict only by escaping into the fog of psychotic denial. Because he had the emotional ability to feel sensitively this pain of unresolvable conflict, he was forced to protect himself from this intolerable agony by severing his contact with reality.

In a similar fashion, a 17 year old psychotic young woman commented on the following statement by her psychotic mother by saying "All I could do was go out of my mind, absolutely stark raving mad!"

> Be independent, make up your mind, be a mature young lady—but tell us everything, and if you don't tell us, get out! How dare you want

215

to leave after all we have done for you! If you don't like it at home, go to a sorority. Why do you have to hurt us so by leaving home? We're glad you got yourself a roommate. We're going to phone her parents to find out what kind of person she is. How dare you make such a fuss! It is a parent's duty to look after their daughter. Get out of the house!

Realistically this young woman loved her psychotic mother because she appreciated that her mother, with all her emotional limitations, cared for her and tried sincerely to do her best. In her growth years, her relationship with two disturbed parents had given this teenager only a very fragmentary ego strength and a poorly developed relationship capability. The mother's destructively ambivalent reaction to her daughter's striving toward independence made the teenager's emotional situation intolerable. As she groped toward a secure personal feminine identification, the identification model provided by her mother was constantly inconstant. The adolescent emancipation struggle became so completely intolerable that this sensitive young woman could relieve her emotional pain only by a withdrawal into her private idiosyncratic psychotic world.

The emancipating teenager is especially vulnerable to the "double bind" situation (Bateson, Jackson, Haley and Weakland, 1956; Weakland, 1960). The teenager who is striving toward independence may be faced not only with a "double bind" but with a "triple bind" dynamic constellation. Not only is he unable to escape from the impossible "double bind" quandary but he is caught in a "triple bind"—he finds that the emotional strength that he has to use in his attempts to escape from such a dilemma is based on totally conflictual early relationships. The more he strives to use his inner emotional resources to deal with an impossible relationship bind, the more he learns that his personality strengths are confused as his early relationships were confused.

When they brought their psychotic fourteen year old son for diagnostic evaluation, his socially prominent parents commented, "We have two choices—either to hospitalize him now or to throw him off a roof."

216

When a human being of any age is faced with such openly destructive feelings in the people who love him and give him direction, these conflicting messages may become so incompatible and the resultant personality so unbearable, that an escape into a psychotic world may be the only means of coping with an otherwise intolerable situation. To face the personal reality of destructively loving parents is unbearable, to face the personal reality of loving murderers is unbearable—withdrawal into an idiosyncratic world makes the situation at least minimally tolerable. In the course of adolescent emancipation, the teenager is faced with the reality that his self-concepts, his self-confidence, and his ego stability are all products of his earliest meaningful relationships. If these relationships were consistently with a loving mother who hated him, the teenager's ego integrity, on which his new emotional independence is founded, must be most insecure and extremely poorly integrated. The process of emancipation which separates the adolescent from environmental supports and direction, throws into much clearer focus the personal significance of past relationships. Early ambiguities and ambivalences once more become painfully experienced. What was barely tolerable in past interactions may become completely unbearable in the clearer focus of the adolescent emotional separation task.

The natural strivings toward adolescent independence may be totally unacceptable to parents who care for their growing child. These loving parents may have been comfortable and accepting of their growing child as a dependent little boy or little girl but when this child becomes an adolescent and seeks independence, such independence may be too unacceptable and too anxiety provoking to the loving parents. The maturing adolescent may be then faced with a decision as to whether he should become independent and lose the parents for whom he deeply cares or whether he should stay dependent and lose his self-respect and his personal integrity. These sensitive adolescents are aware of the goals and the rewards of their culture and their peer society; they may wish earnestly to grow toward these ideals and these levels of maturation. When such an adolescent who does have the ability to relate meaningfully is faced with such an unbearable choice, he may resolve this emotional dilemma by withdrawing in a reactive psychotic process.

THE RESIDENTIAL TREATMENT PROGRAM WITH THE REACTIVE PSYCHOTIC ADOLESCENT

Since the disturbed, reactive psychotic adolescent is reacting with a process of psychotic withdrawal to an unstable, unpredictable environment, the residential treatment setting must first provide him with a stable, certain environmental consistency. The disturbed teenager became psychotic when he discovered that his natural growth drive produced environmental rejection; thus the treatment milieu must support the natural growth process in this patient in a kindly, encouraging fashion that does not push the adolescent beyond his realistic capabilities. In repeated daily interaction, the reactive psychotic adolescent must learn that meaningful people in a stable environment will appreciate and find personal gratification in his growth and his achievement. As Carter (1942) points out, it is this continued ability to relate that makes these patients much more available to a meaningful treatment process.

While the treatment staff understand the disturbed teenager's weaknesses and limitations, the therapeutic focus is placed on the potential of the reactive psychotic adolescent for growth and development. In this way, the treatment team can begin to demonstrate to the adolescent himself how his own behavior patterns may have been influential in perpetuating and accentuating the instability and the uncertainty of his total environment. He needs to discover how his own reactions may have contributed to the disrupting tensions of his family and his culture. In a constant treatment environment which provides approval for realistic striving and growth, the secondary gratifications for psychotic withdrawal are in this way minimized. Rewards and approval are given for reaching out and for trying.

218

Daniel was an attractive 16 year old psychotic boy. He was the only son of a wealthy family and had been emotionally very close to his mother all his life. For two years prior to his hospital admission he had remained completely at home lest he become infected by germs. He did not associate with other children whom he felt did not like him and had unclean sexual impulses toward him. He did not go to school because he considered that his teachers were vindictively victimizing him.

Following his hospital admission, his mother's letters would constantly refer to him as "my beloved," "my honey," and "my sweetheart." In detail, she discussed at length how much she "missed your arms around my neck." Invariably his father was too busy either to write letters or to be directly involved with his son.

After his admission to the treatment unit, Daniel went through a period of well publicized agony. Though he steadfastly maintained that he wished to remain in hospital and grow toward health, his letters home repeatedly detailed the misery of his unloved existence in the residential setting. It was necessary to give his mother consistent specific direction and support so that she could maintain him in the hospital. In the hospital school, Daniel presented himself as a consistent, inevitable failure, though his intelligence level was in the superior range. He started off by pleading with his teachers for leniency and by maintaining pathetically that he was physically incapable of performing even the most limited school work. Repeatedly he successfully manipulated his very empathic teachers into doing his school work for him. With his peer group, he quickly made himself the focus of sexualized jokes in which the other boys would ridicule him for his feminine mannerism. Daniel wore the martyr's crown with a great deal of emotional satisfaction.

In the stable residential environment, the first task of the treatment personnel was to minimize the gratification Daniel was obviously receiving from his continued psychotic behavior. The members of the treatment team empathized with his ego inadequacies and with his anxiety but steadfastly did not reward him for his incapacities. When he sought and gained attention through making a fool of himself, he was removed from the group setting. The staff members worked with him so that he could see how his own inner tensions prompted him to become the clown. With direct supervision it was no longer necessary for his teachers to do his homework for him. They began to give due appreciation for whatever he attempted and wherever he succeeded. Quickly it became obvious that this young man did indeed relish approval from the people he respected and liked.

In the ongoing casework process, Daniel's parents were gradually helped to gain pleasure from his successes as a very personable young man. Slowly, over a four year process, this adolescent boy was able to give up his psychotic reaction pattern and to evolve for himself a comfortable adjustment to everyday peer society. With some anxiety and appropriate mourning, his parents agreed that, rather than return home to a setting which he might still find regressive, Daniel should move from the hospital environment to a college dormitory where he could continue his emotional growth toward independence and final self-sufficiency.

Where these reactive psychotic adolescents are given a warm, stable, growth promoting environment, they can usually allow themselves very gradually to emerge from their psychotic retreat. The caring staff must take care lest they react too precipitously to the teenage patient's very tentative early attempts to interact. The treatment process must be very slow and gradual so that the adolescent patient is neither overburdened nor hurt emotionally. By necessary repetitious experimentation these teenage patients find out that their environment and the people in their environment are trustworthy. If these young men and women are not too stunted emotionally, or if their psychotic process has not become egosyntonic, frequently they show rapid growth in ego development and in relationship capability. Once they reach the stage of beginning to trust again, they may in a matter of months move rapidly from a psychotic reaction pattern to an emotional status where they show only moderate neurotic handicapping. As in most treatment processes with other patients, the longest time in the treatment process is taken in encouraging and in supporting the uncertain patient to begin to try and to start to trust.

An individualized psychotherapy process may provide the central treatment focus in the total therapeutic program for the reactive psychotic adolescent. Since these teenagers are emotionally disturbed because of disturbed relationships, a consistent, reconstructive psychotherapy interaction may prove of maximum benefit. In an individualized psychotherapy relationship, the psychotherapist must first establish a consistent, warm accepting interaction. The uncertain fragile adolescent will have to test the stability and the certainty of this individualized relationship over a period of months or even years before he can allow himself to trust himself to trust the psychotherapist. In the privacy of these individual psychotherapy sessions, the reactive psychotic adolescent may make his first feeble attempts to reach out meaningfully once more. Only when the psychotherapy relationship bond is established and has become a source of definite strength for the patient, can the psychotherapist begin very gently to interpret some of the underlying conflicts and anxieties that have led to the teenage patient's psychotic withdrawal. If the psychotherapist has gauged the time accurately for these tentative interpretations, the teenage patient should now have sufficient ego strength in himself and in the psychotherapy bond to face some of his conflictual anxiety without psychotic withdrawal. In this psychotherapy treatment relationship, the teenage patient and his psychotherapist should then be able to face together the terrors of these conflicts and work out a better solution. If such a psychotherapeutic process can help the teenager resolve some of his underlying conflicts, the emotional energy freed will increasingly strengthen the teenager's basic ego capabilities so that he can more readily discard those psychotic defenses that still persist. Once these teenage patients develop sufficient trust in themselves and in the treatment relationship, the individual psychotherapy relationship can deepen quickly in emotional significance and growth potential.

Where the adolescent does not have the emotional strength to tolerate an interpretive process, premature interpretation may cause increased regression and more overt psychosis. The psychotherapist and the treatment team members must take this regression as a vitally important diagnostic-treatment cue; they must revert to their slow steady task of strengthening the teenage patient's ego and self-confidence before they attempt any further interpretive-reconstructive measures. In dealing with some reactive psychotic teenagers, the therapeutic team learn that an interpretive treatment process is never therapeutically advisable because the teenager's ego strengths never develop to the point where his underlying emotional conflicts become manageable. These more uncertain adolescents may maintain a lifelong reactive psychotic pattern where they still have the ability to relate sensitively; more often their psychotic reaction becomes increasingly egosyntonic and a process schizophrenic character state evolves. At this stage the psychotic teenager has ceased to care about the relationships that formerly caused him pain; he is comfortable in his own private world.

As the adolescent patient begins to give up his psychotic defenses, usually his outward behavior becomes markedly compulsive. He has only been able to start trusting because he has been sure of environmental stability. As he allows himself to interact openly with his environment and with those around him, he must stabilize this environmental consistency by himself becoming markedly obsessive. In his first awkward efforts to relate openly, he must have the stability and the certainty of constant repetitive compulsive patterns of living. In this transition stage from inner directed psychosis to outer directed relating, the teenager's interaction with his environment may appear to become much less rich. During his florid psychotic state, his room may have been filled with possessions scattered around in grossly disorganized abandon; as he begins to relate realistically and meaningfully, it is quite likely that his surroundings will become bare and rigidly organized. As the disturbed teenager brings his emotions under control and starts to involve himself meaningfully with people, he will grow through this stage where he has to keep his feelings and his environment totally and rigidly in check. If his inner tensions mount beyond his ability to control, his behavior may again become floridly expressive but more overtly disorganized. If he continues to control his inner anxieties and increases his ego growth, gradually his compulsive defenses will soften and he will show increasing self-expression and flexibility in his interactions, in his behavior, and in his surroundings.

The treatment program for the reactive psychotic adolescent patient requires the most intensive, sensitive team involvement and integration. The total therapeutic focus must be on the teenager's individual capabilities and growth potential. In a stable integrated treatment environment, many of these reactive psychotic teenagers have the emotional capability to give up their psychotic pattern of relating and gradually to return to a meaningful productive role within their family and their community.

Chapter XI

The Goals and the Results of
Residential Treatment

If the therapeutic investment by the teenage patient, by the family of the adolescent patient, and by the treatment staff, is to be of any permanent value, the treatment program must be directed toward specific, realistic goals. In planning the best therapeutic approach for the individual adolescent, the caring staff must take into consideration what the adolescent *can* do, what he is *willing* to do and what the environmental circumstances will *allow* him to do.

Very frequently, a teenage patient comes to an inpatient treatment process after years of repeated, personal traumatization and resultant emotional stunting. These adolescents live with the self-concept that they are bad, malevolent, or totally unacceptable. Many disturbed adolescents, who are already severely limited emotionally, and profoundly handicapped intellectually, need above all the enriching growth experience of being accepted and appreciated at the realistic level of their social and emotional capabilities. In a productive therapeutic environment, these teenagers are accepted as they are and the treatment goals for them are sensibly based on the strengths and the potentials they possess. As these disturbed adolescents have grown, their emotional stunting and their intellectual distortion has been accentuated and perpetuated by unrealistic environmental demands. In the inpatient setting, these young men and young women are now involved in a treatment alliance where they themselves have the final decision as to the direction in which they will grow and what responsibilities they can reasonably assume. The main purpose for any treatment process is to help these unhappy teenagers to grow as far as they can grow.

When these patients enter a therapeutic program after years of emotional disturbance, the treatment aims must be based on a thorough evaluation of their present strengths and on an understanding of their past history. For the preadolescent child, the treatment goal usually is to return him to his family, if this family environment is emotionally accepting and growth oriented. Since the task of the normal adolescent is to emancipate and to become independent, the treatment goal with the disturbed adolescent is not to reunite him completely with his family but to help him become intellectually and emotionally independent and, as well as he is able, to function as a productive member of society. It must be emphasized that the final goal with the normal and the disturbed adolescent is realistic separation and appropriate independence. During the treatment process, the teenager and his family must be helped to work together to face the feelings that disturb them as a family, but this working together has the long-term eventual goal of meaningful separation and mutual independence.

As these disturbed adolescents in the inpatient setting move toward a healthier adaptation, they begin to realize what they have missed and what they will never obtain. So often, during the course of productive treatment, these teenagers begin to appreciate the emotional significance of warm, meaningful family interactions, only to become reacquainted with the bitter reality that, within their family and within their social environment, they can never achieve such relationships. In the treatment process, the caring personnel must never raise hopes that cannot be fulfilled. It would be both cruel and destructive to promise such an adolescent a happy integrated home and a warm accepting family. In reality, these teenagers are now too old to be completely reunited within a family. Their adolescent task is to emancipate from the family unit; hopefully they can grow and mature emotionally so that they will be able to develop the emotional capabilities necessary to establish a new family of their own in their future adult roles.

You bastards have surely made my life Hell. All you did was to get me to want a family and you knew all along I could never have one.

This bitter statement by a sad and angry, adolescent girl highlights this treatment dilemma with the disturbed adolescent. If these patients are to move emotionally toward health and adult self-sufficiency, they must give up the hope of a warm, dependent, childlike relationship with parenting figures. They can never relive their childhood and recover emotional relationships they missed, unless they regress into illness. Once these teenagers decide to grow toward a healthier, age-appropriate emotional competency, they must relinquish their childhood dreams and hopes. In this growth process, they must mourn with appropriate sadness and with reasonable anger the loss of what should have been. Such a natural mourning process allows them to plan for the years to come when they themselves can be parents and can establish the kind of family that they missed in their younger years.

As these uncertain teenagers wrestle with their unresolved dependency and emancipation needs, they experience deep longings for warm, loving relationships. At all times the individual experience of hospitalization is a profoundly lonely period of emotional suffering for any teenager for whom relationships are meaningful but this loneliness is especially acute at the periods of family celebration. If these disturbed adolescents have the emotional ability to care but lack a warm, stable family or the self-control to allow them to function within a family environment, their stay in the inpatient milieu over Christmas, Thanksgiving or their birthdays is especially agonizing. In most residential units, these times of normal family rejoicing are the most difficult and depressing periods of the inpatient treatment year. It is true that the therapeutic team cannot completely provide these sad and lonely young men and young women with the deep warmth and sharing that usually envelops a family unit during Christmas, Hanukkah, or Thanksgiving. However the caring staff can offer sincere empathy for the deep personal loneliness of these adolescent patients, thereby helping them to bear their agony and hopefully giving them the support which will ultimately allow them to establish deeper emotional relationships in the future.

As the preadolescent inpatient moves back into the ordinary social community, it is frequently helpful to place him in a foster care home or a boarding home. For the adolescent patient, especially the older adolescent, such a treatment move is often not possible. Many family care homes are not suitable for the older teenager. The foster home parents, who provide such family-care services for the financial inducements, are frequently young and too near in age to the older adolescent. On the other hand, the boarding home parents may be elderly and unable to provide sufficiently flexible parental identification models for the maturing teenager. The potential boarding home parents, who have teenage children of their own and who could most competently handle the disturbed adolescent as he matures, usually have sufficient financial resources so that they do not need the extra money brought by providing a family-care home for a former hospital patient.

The presence of other teenagers in a boarding home family will raise therapeutic problems which the teenage patient may not be able to tolerate. As the adolescent tries hesitantly to move from the hospital back into society, the competition with a healthy adolescent in the same home may be too much to bear; the presence of a teenager of the opposite sex in the same house may arouse impulses which are difficult to control with the limited emotional resources available to the former inpatient. A family-care home frequently cannot provide the careful supervision that the emotionally maturing patient requires and can tolerate, without forcing him into too dependent a role. Many older adolescent inpatients reject the offer of a boarding home placement which they see as an illogical, regressive step in their maturation and emancipation. As a hirsute 17 year old young man stated, "I'm too old to have a Daddy."

The successful completion of an inpatient treatment process may mean that the older adolescent moves to a college dormitory, to an individual apartment or to an apartment shared with friends, to the Armed Services, or to a group-living setting such as the Y.M.C.A. In very specific instances, with carefully selected adolescents, it may be possible to place the teenage patient in a foster home but such a placement takes a most unusual home and an unusually flexible young patient. The growth-supporting therapeutic possibilities outside the inpatient hospital environment are most limited for the young adolescent who is not old enough to be totally independent yet who does not have a suitable natural or foster home setting to which he can go. Many of these younger teenage patients could most productively use a loosely supervised group boarding-home environment as a continued maturation experience. If these patients of high school age are maintained in hospital after they are emotionally ready to leave, this prolonged hospitalization may cause loss of emotional growth. On the other hand, premature total emancipation may overburden the young teenager's emotional capability and may force personality disintegration or behavioral regression. For this group of younger adolescents who are ready to leave the hospital environment but have no home to which they can go, posthospitalization treatment facilities are especially inadequate and unsatisfactory.

There is a significant group of older teenage patients who have matured to a point where they no longer require the total inpatient support but who still lack the emotional capability necessary to function in total independence. The treatment prospects for these young men and women are extremely unsatisfactory. Many of these older adolescents, who do not need continual around-the-clock hospital support, still require the growth support and the strengthening that they could receive in a sheltered workshop. If such a young man or young woman could be placed and maintained in a supervised factory setting, it is quite likely that he or she would continue to grow emotionally and productively. A sheltered college environment would provide a continued maturation experience for the emotionally limited adolescent of higher intellectual capability but such treatment-supportive academic facilities are markedly lacking. For many former inpatients, the entrance to college is difficult because of their uneven scholastic background and the hesitancy of the college administrations to admit the former mental patient. At this time, there are only very limited opportunities to provide growth continuity and social support when these older adolescents move from the hospital setting into the general adult society. This lack of community facilities tends to perpetuate unnecessary institutionalization and to maintain unhealthy patterns of hospital-oriented adaptation. Without social support for their continued growth, these former inpatients tend to gravitate emotionally to other former patients and to social outcasts.

The final treatment goals for each teenage patient must be individually planned on the basis of his personal capabilities. If the autistic child matures emotionally to the point where he can go to a public school, even part-time, this level of functioning indicates amazing treatment success. This very handicapped adolescent may have to continue in a sheltered environment for the rest of his life but, within his emotional and intellectual limitations, he will have grown remarkably in the inpatient treatment process. If a severely infantile adolescent is no longer prone to disruptive tantrums in his routine social interactions, he has made significant emotional advances which may allow him to maintain himself productively in society. If the basically psychotic teenager has so mustered his ego strength that he can contain his inner psychotic process and can function without disturbance in an ordinary community setting, he has made outstanding treatment advances which may permit him to be a productive member of society (Rutter and Lockyer, 1967). Many disturbed adolescents can only grow and mature to a moderate extent with the limited emotional and intellectual resources they possess. To continue to push the teenage patient to take responsibility beyond his growth capability is a most insensitive, cruel, and totally non-therapeutic treatment approach. This environmental pressure and expectation, without realistic regard for the individual teenager's basic capabilities, may so overburden him that emotional regression and disintegration are produced.

Not only may these handicapped adolescents have to face the lack of community support for their continued growth and emancipation but frequently they have to deal very directly with the lack of family encouragement for their continued emotional development. If the teenage boy acquires personal sensitivities and capabilities beyond those of his parents and his family, his continued emotional growth will cause mounting family anxiety and, in many instances, eventual rejection by his family. If the formerly promiscuous teenage girl develops a conscience that is more feminine and more sensitive than the conscience of her mother, the anxiety aroused in her mother by the relationship with her daughter may cause the mother to reject the teenage girl. If the young adolescent male patient shows more natural masculine aggressiveness than his father, he may find that his father cannot tolerate this comparison or this implied competition. Typically the maturing teenager, by virtue of his increasing competence and capabilities, highlights the defects and the limitations in his own family in a fashion which the family members cannot tolerate. The teenager's parents may not appreciate or understand the underlying cause for their increasing anxiety but they may find themselves acting in an angry, destructive, rejecting fashion toward their adolescent who is showing this emotional growth within the treatment process. A distraught mother

230

described with much emotional pain, the reason why she could not allow her adolescent son to visit home on any future vacations.

> He used to be so cuddly and cute. We used to cozy up together and share our secrets. Now he is all hair and muscles. I can't stand him!

In reality, after only six months in an inpatient setting, this young man had developed sufficient masculine self-respect and self-assertiveness to highlight, in a fashion that his mother could not tolerate, the frankly erotized relationship his mother had maintained with him in the past. Because of his emotional growth and improvement, this adolescent was no longer tolerable in his own home.

As these teenage patients grow toward health and maturity, quite frequently they find that they must make the emotional choice between their own family or their own self-sufficiency. Many disturbed teenagers, when they have this choice of either giving up their illness or their family, decide to remain emotionally ill so that at least they can continue to be part of a family, albeit a sick family.

> After a Thanksgiving visit home, a 16 year old boy announced that he was withdrawing himself from public school where, until that time, he was doing remarkably well. He withdrew to his room after this announcement and would say little for several days. Eventually he confided to a trusted child-care worker.

> My old lady likes me crazy. When I stop being crazy, she doesn't know what to say to me and I don't know what to say to her. The house gets so lonely that we have to go back to being our old selves—crazy, but man, we're not lonely then.

In their work with the individual adolescent patient, the treatment team must always appreciate the emotional price the teenager has to pay for personality changes and readjustments. The process of emotional growth not only implies change and strengthening but also the giving up of former emotional ties and identification models. For some disturbed teenagers, this price is more than they can be reasonably asked to pay.

PREMATURE CHARACTER SOLIDIFICATION AS AN EMOTIONAL SOLUTION

During the adolescent decade, the normal teenager grows and experiments. He tries out various forms of relationships and different character patterns. As he develops into adulthood, his personal character begins to solidify and his emotional reaction patterns become more stabilized. By the middle of the third decade of life, the individual personality structure is fairly solid and relatively immutable. The young adult is accustomed to himself and comfortable with his personality.

In dealing with the adolescent patient, the caring staff may have to face the reality that many disturbed adolescents have already established a relatively stable, unchangeable character structure by the time they are 15 or 16 years old. The teenager may say defiantly, "I am pleased with the way I am," and he may be totally realistic and honest. This premature character solidification is a common defense maneuver whereby the disturbed adolescent can relieve his emotional pain and can make his limitations bearable (Shainberg, 1966).

Where the teenager has the experience of being repeatedly and painfully rejected, the resultant personal anxiety can become almost unbearable. This pain and tension becomes tolerable if the adolescent decides that he is really a "loner"—he no longer has to worry or grieve about being rejected because characterologically he is not really interested in relationships anyhow. His character solidification has relieved his ego anxiety.

If a disturbed teenager is chronically inadequate emotionally, and persistently anxious and uncertain, he may minimize the pain of his ego inadequacy by making permanent the character state of being inadequate. If he allows himself the fixed identity of inadequacy, he no longer has to struggle over his deficiencies—since he is inadequate he is not really lacking or deficient anymore. If he agrees with himself that he is simply unable to handle responsibilities, his personality weaknesses no longer upset him because inadequacy becomes a steady way of life, a definite character status.

By mid-adolescence, many disturbed teenagers, who have only inadequate personality resources, relieve their ego tensions and evolve a method of functioning by stabilizing their character structure at the level of sickness. When this early character solidification does occur, it may be impossible to produce further characterological shifts, regardless of the treatment process. Where the treatment team appreciates that such an emotional stratification and solidification has occurred, they must then decide, in the treatment alliance with the teenager, how to help him live with this more fixed character state. Many disturbed adolescents will try to give the impression to those around them that they made a conscious deliberate decision in favor of this premature character solidification. In reality this early personality fixation is liable to occur automatically and almost inevitably in teenagers with very limited ego resources and a relatively high titer of anxiety and emotional pain. In order to cope, these teenage patients may have little emotional alternative but to settle for a lifetime characterological distortion.

The treatment team must face the constant reality that the final treatment outcome with each teenage patient is dependent on the emotional sensitivities and capabilities of the adolescent, on his ability and potential to use environmental strengths and supports, and on his willingness to participate in any growth-oriented treatment process. The adolescent may be consciously very ready to enter into a treatment process but may find that the emotional changes produced by such a therapeutic program raise intolerable anxieties or produce unbearable environmental tensions which will minimize the possibilities for change. In such a situation the adolescent and the treatment team will have to settle for more limited treatment goals.

RESULTS OF THE INPATIENT TREATMENT OF THE DISTURBED ADOLESCENT

In his review of reports on the inpatient treatment of adolescents, Beskind (1962) points out the dearth of useful clinical papers on the results and the prognosis of residential treatment. In most of the recent presentations (Sands, 1953; Masterson, 1956; Annesley, 1961; Craft, Stephenson, and Granger, 1964; Klapman, Slagle, and Morino, 1964; Bashina, 1965; Pollack, Levenstein, and Klein, 1968), the diagnostic and the clinical criteria of the patients described are often not clearly defined and, if such background information is given, the teenage patients usually differ so widely between the treatment centers that a comparison is not fully possible. The adolescent patient groups reported in these papers tend to be so small that statistical comparisons are not possible within the individual groups or between the groups reported. In these published reports, there is usually no discussion about the appropriateness, specificity, or benefit that different treatment programs provided different adolescent patient groups. Since the results of treatment in an inpatient setting can be both growth-promoting as well as growth-stunting, it can be suggested that some of the unfortunate treatment results were due to inappropriate inpatient treatment and not to the original illness. Insofar as many emotionally resilient adolescent patients get better in spite of an institutionalized therapeutic regimen, it is difficult to ascertain from these published papers where any therapeutic benefit originated. Hospital placement has a severely debilitating effect on certain emotionally vulnerable teenagers who would have been much better helped in other treatment environments. When the treatment results with the disturbed adolescent are evaluated, it is necessary to consider first whether the treatment was planned for the patient or the patient for the treatment.

The diagnostic and treatment approach described in this monograph is based largely on the author's experience at the Menninger Foundation. In the eight years since the expansion of the Children's Hospital of the Menninger Foundation to offer facilities for disturbed adolescents, there has been insufficient patient turnover to justify meaningful tabulation and statistical comparison. The author would merely detail his

personal impressions from the patients evaluated and discussed in this book.

About four out of every five severely neurotic hospitalized
teenagers grow emotionally in the treatment process to some
level of acceptable social adaptation. Approximately 50 per
cent of these neurotic teenagers mature to the point where
they would be considered to be within the continuum of social
normality following their hospital discharge. The other teenagers in this group who achieve social adaptation continue
overly impulsive, phobic, or anxious but at a level where they
can function in society. Some neurotically disturbed adolescents maintain a neurotic character structure as their most acceptable method of adaptation. They portray themselves as
"worriers," as being chronically depressed, or as being per-
petually fearful. Most neurotic inpatients appear to separate
efficiently from their former hospital environment. They are
able emotionally to leave their hospital identity behind them
at the time of their discharge.

While about 80 per cent of the adolescents admitted with
ego developmental arrest return to general society, probably
only 20 to 30 per cent of these teenagers maintain themselves
at a fully acceptable level of adult social adjustment. The
majority in this group function only at a marginal level of
community adaptation. Most of these ego-limited patients continue to have problems with alcohol, with marriage, or with
the law. Many maintain ties with hospital personnel, with
former fellow patients, and with the institution itself. Frequently, this adolescent patient group perpetuates and maintains a narcissistically based patient culture outside the hospital. The most infantile teenagers may be unable to develop
sufficient ego strength to live apart from a protected environment. Approximately 20 per cent of these adolescents with
severely arrested ego development continue in a hospital environment or in a protecting institution such as a prison.
These teenagers may well force their discharge from hospital
but later so involve themselves with legal authorities that they

are again removed from the community and placed in a sheltered, structured setting.

The process psychotic teenager has the worst prognosis of all adolescent inpatients. Approximately 50 per cent of these very severely disturbed teenagers continue to live in a custodial long-term hospital setting or in some equally sheltered, structured environment. Only about 20 per cent of these process psychotic patients return to society in a self-supporting capacity, while approximately 30 per cent maintain a marginal social existence with close, firm community support. The disturbed adolescent who presents with a reactive schizophrenic process has a much better treatment prognosis. Probably about half of these patients return to everyday living within the range of emotional normality, while 25 per cent mature to the point where they can maintain themselves in society at a moderately neurotic level of functioning. The remaining 25 per cent of these reactive schizophrenic patients, and especially those who develop a process psychotic reaction as an emotional defense, continue so handicapped that they need the constant day-to-day structuring provided either within a hospital setting or within the context of the social role described as the "intermittent patient" (Friedman, von Mering, and Hinko, 1966). The adolescent patient who is admitted with a schizophrenic process is liable to maintain some continued ties to his former inpatient setting after his discharge. These ties may be emotionally necessary if he is to maintain his internalized representation of meaningful hospital relationships and structures which hopefully will allow him to remain functioning outside the hospital wall.

* * *

In view of the intensive and expensive treatment process described in these chapters, such treatment results may appear to be somewhat depressing. However, it must be borne in mind that the adolescent patients highlighted in these pages are among the most seriously ill and the least promising therapeutically in all psychiatric practice. Usually they are the rejects and the failures from a succession of diagnostic and treatment processes. A deeper understanding of these severely disturbed young men and women can give us a wider appreciation of the etiological, diagnostic, therapeutic, and prognostic problems raised with all adolescents. Further investigation with both the well-adjusted and the acutely disturbed adolescent is needed to clarify for mental health workers the process of teenage development.

As the author was writing this final chapter, he received a letter from a former patient who had spent three years in the hospital inpatient setting; this adolescent summed up for himself and for the writer the total purpose of treatment—in the words of Kierkegaard:

> "To venture is to risk anxiety, but not
> to venture is to lose yourself."

References

Aichhorn, A. (1964), On the Technique of Child Guidance: The Narcissistic Transference of the "Juvenile Imposter." In: *Delinquency and Child Guidance.* New York: International Universities Press, pp. 174-191.

Alderton, H. (1963), Reactive Psychosis in Adolescence. *Canad. Psychiat. Assn. J.,* 8:255-266.

—— (1965), Communication, Learning and Therapeutic Process in a Children's Psychiatric Hospital. *Canad. Psychiat. Assoc. J.,* 10:338-349.

—— (1967), The Role of Punishment in the Inpatient Treatment of Psychiatrically Disturbed Children. *Canad. Psychiat. Assoc. J.,* 12:17-24.

Almond, R. and Esser, A. H. (1965), Tablemate Choices of Psychiatric Patients. *J. Nerv. & Ment. Dis.,* 141:68-82.

Alt, H. (1960), *Residential Treatment for the Disturbed Child.* New York: International Universities Press.

Annesley, P. T. (1961), Psychiatric Illness in Adolescence: Presentation and Prognosis. *J. Ment. Sci.,* 107:268-278.

Anthony, E. J. and Scott, P. (1960), Manic Depressive Psychosis in Childhood. *J. Child Psychol. & Psychiat.,* 1:53-72.

Balser, B. H. and Masterson, J. F. (1959), Suicide in Adolescents. *Amer. J. Psychiat.,* 116:400-404.

Barton, R. (1966), *Institutional Neurosis* (second edition). Bristol: Wright.

Bashina, V. M. (1965), The Work Capacity and Social Adaptation of Schizophrenic Patients Who Became Ill in Childhood and Adolescence. *Internat. J. Psychiat.,* 1:248-257.

Bateson, G., Jackson, D. D., Haley, J., and Weakland, J. H. (1956), Towards a Theory of Schizophrenia. *Behavior. Sci.,* 1:251-264.

Beck, J. C., Macht, L. B., Levinson, D. J., and Strauss, M. (1967), A Controlled Experimental Study of the Therapist-Administrator Split. *Amer. J. Psychiat.,* 124:467-474.

Beckett, P. G. S. (1965), *Adolescents Out of Step.* Detroit: Wayne State University Press.

Beskind, H. (1962), Psychiatric Inpatient Treatment of Adolescents. *Comprehen. Psychiat.,* 3:354-369.

Bettelheim, B. (1966), Training the Child Care Worker in a Residential Center. *Amer. J. Orthopsychiat.,* 36:694-705.

239

—— and Sylvester, E. (1947), Therapeutic Influence of the Group on the Individual. *Amer. J. Orthopsychiat.,* 17:684-692.

—— and —— (1948), A Therapeutic Milieu. *Amer. J. Orthopsychiat.,* 18:191-206.

Blackman, N., Weiss, J. M. A., and Lamberti, J. W. (1963), The Sudden Murderer. *Arch. Gen. Psychiat.,* 8:289-294.

Brody, E. B. (1960), Borderline State, Character Disorder and Psychotic Manifestations—Some Conceptual Formulations. *Psychiat.,* 23:75-80.

Cameron, K. (1953), Group Approach to Inpatient Adolescents. *Amer. J. Psychiat.,* 109:657-661.

Caplan, L. M. (1966), Identification, A Complicating Factor in the Inpatient Treatment of Adolescent Girls. *Amer. J. Orthopsychiat.,* 36:720-724.

Carek, D. J., Hendrickson, W. J., and Holmes, D. J. (1961), Delinquency Addiction in Parents. *Arch. Gen. Psychiat.,* 4:357-362.

Carter, A. B. (1942), The Prognostic Factors of Adolescent Psychoses. *J. Ment. Sci.,* 88:31-81.

Christ, A. E. and Wagner, N. N. (1966), Iatrogenic Factors in Residential Treatment: A Problem in Staff Training. *Amer. J. Orthopsychiat.,* 36:725-729.

Chwast, J. (1967), Depressive Reactions as Manifested among Adolescent Delinquents. *Amer. J. Psychother.,* 21:575-584.

Cohen, R. L. (1963), Developments in the Isolation Therapy of Behavior Disorders of Children. In: *Current Psychiatric Therapies.* Vol. 3, ed. J. H. Masserman. New York: Grune & Stratton, pp. 180-187.

—— and Grinspoon, L. (1963), Limit Setting as a Corrective Ego Experience. *Arch. Gen. Psychiat.,* 8:74-79.

Counts, R. M. (1967), Family Crises and the Impulsive Adolescent. *Arch. Gen. Psychiat.,* 17:64-71.

Craft, M., Stephenson, G., and Granger, C. (1964), A Controlled Trial of Authoritarian and Self-Governing Regimes with Adolescent Psychopaths. *Amer. J. Orthopsychiat.,* 34:543-554.

Curran, F. J. (1939), Organization of a Ward for Adolescents in Bellevue Psychiatric Hospital. *Amer. J. Psychiat.,* 95:1365-1388.

Dettelbach, M. H. (1955), Criteria for Agency Referral of a Child to a Residential Treatment Center. *Amer. J. Orthopsychiat.,* 25:669-674.

Easson, W. M. (1966), The Ego-Ideal in the Treatment of Children and Adolescents. *Arch. Gen. Psychiat.,* 15:288-292.

—— (1967a), Adolescent Environments Reveal Diagnostic Cues. *Hosp. Commun. Psychiat.,* 18:119-121.

—— (1967b), Adolescent Inpatients in Love—A Therapeutic Contradiction. *Arch. Gen. Psychiat.,* 16:758-763.

—— (1967c), The Continued Non-Patient, An Adolescent Dilemma. *Arch. Gen. Psychiat.,* 16:359-363.

—— (1967d), Projection as an Etiological Factor in "Motiveless" Delinquency. *Psychiat. Quart.,* 41:228-232.

—— (1967e), The Anaclitic Ego Deficiency Syndrome of Adolescence. *Adolescence,* 2:97-106.

—— (1968), Ego Defects in NonPsychotic Adolescents. *Psychiat. Quart.,* 42:156-168.

Edwalds, R. and Dimitri, K. (1959), Treatment of the Adolescent Patient in a State Hospital. *Psychiat. Quart.*, 33:615-622.

Engel, M. (1960), Shifting Levels of Communication in Treatment of Adolescent Character Disorders. *Arch. Gen. Psychiat.*, 2:94-99.

Fairbairn, W. R. D. (1952), *Psychoanalytic Studies of the Personality*. London: Tavistock.

Felix, R. H. (1961), Proceedings, 1961. Annual Conference, Surgeon General, Public Health Service with State and Territorial Mental Health Authorities. Washington, D.C.: Public Health Service Publication 851.

Fish, B. (1968), Drug Use in Psychiatric Disorders of Children. *Amer. J. Psychiat.*, 124. Feb. Suppl., 31-36.

Freedman, A. M. and Bender, L. (1957), When the Childhood Schizophrenic Grows Up. *Amer. J. Orthopsychiat.*, 27:553-565.

Friedman, I., von Mering, O., and Hinko, E. N. (1966), Intermittent Patienthood. *Arch. Gen. Psychiat.*, 14:386-392.

Gedo, J. E. (1966), The Psychotherapy of Developmental Arrest. *Brit. J. Med. Psychol.*, 39:25-33.

Gilbert, A. (1965), Editorial: Adolescents in State Hospitals: Expensive Expediency. *Amer. J. Orthopsychiat.*, 35:825-827.

Glaser, K. (1965), Suicide in Children and Adolescents. In: *Acting Out—Theoretical and Clinical Aspects*, eds. L. E. Abt and S. L. Weisman. New York: Grune & Stratton, pp. 87-99.

Goldsmith, J. M. (1963), The Problem as Hawthorne Sees It. *J. Amer. Acad. Child Psychiat.*, 2:510-519.

Greaves, D. C. and Regan, P. F. (1957), Psychotherapy of Adolescents at Intensive Hospital Treatment Level. In: *Psychotherapy of the Adolescent*, ed. B. H. Balser. New York: International Universities Press, pp. 130-143.

Greenson, R. R. (1954), The Struggle against Identification. *J. Amer. Psychoanal. Assoc.*, 2:200-217.

Grinker, R. R. (1962), "Mentally Healthy" Young Males (Homoclites). *Arch. Gen. Psychiat.*, 6:405-453.

Hendrickson, W. J. and Holmes, D. J. (1959), Control of Behavior as a Crucial Factor in an All Adolescent Ward. *Amer. J. Psychiat.*, 115:969-973.

——, ——, and Waggoner, R. W. (1959), Psychotherapy of the Hospitalized Adolescent. *Amer. J. Psychiat.* 116:527-532.

Higgins, J. (1964), The Concept of Process-Reactive Schizophrenia: Criteria and Related Research. *J. Nerv. & Ment. Dis.*, 138:9-25.

Hirschberg, J. C. and Mandelbaum, A. (1957), Problems of Administration and Supervision in an Inpatient Treatment Center for Children. *Bull. Menn. Clin.*, 21:208-219.

Holmes, D. J. (1964), *The Adolescent in Psychotherapy*. Boston: Little, Brown and Co.

Inglis, D. (1963), Authority and Reality in Residential Treatment. Paper presented at the Annual Meeting of the American Association of Children's Residential Centers, Chicago.

Jacobziner, H. (1965), Attempted Suicides in Adolescents by Poisoning. *Amer. J. Psychother.*, 19:247-252.

Johnson, A. M. (1949), Sanctions for Superego Lacunae of Adolescents. In: *Searchlights on Delinquency*, ed. K. Eissler. New York: International Universities Press, pp. 225-245.

Kantor, R. E. and Herron, W. G. (1966), *Reactive and Process Schizophrenia.* Palo Alto: Science and Behavior Books, Inc.

Kasanin, J. and Kaufman, M. R. (1929), A Study of the Functional Psychoses in Childhood. *Amer. J. Psychiat.*, 86:307-384.

Kellam, S. G. and Chassan, J. (1962), Social Context and Symptom Fluctuation. *Psychiat.*, 25:370-381.

——, Shmelzer, J. L., and Berman, A. (1966), Variations in the Atmospheres of Psychiatric Wards. *Arch. Gen. Psychiat.*, 14:561-570.

Klapman, H., Slagle, S. and Morino, I. (1964), Rehabilitation of Children Discharged from a Psychiatric Hospital. *Amer. J. Orthopsychiat.*, 34:942-947.

Klein, M. (1952), Notes on Some Schizoid Mechanisms. In: *Developments in Psychoanalysis*, ed. J. Riviere. London: Hogarth, pp. 292-320.

Konopka, G. (1955), The Role of the Group in Residential Treatment. *Amer. J. Orthopsychiat.*, 25:679-684.

—— (1961), Changes in the Group Living Situation. *Amer. J. Orthopsychiat.*, 31: 32-39.

Kraft, I. A. (1968), The Use of Psychoactive Drugs in the Outpatient Treatment of Psychiatric Disorders of Children. *Amer. J. Psychiat.*, 124:1401-1407.

Lewin, K. K. (1965), Non-verbal Cues and Transference. *Arch. Gen. Psychiat.*, 12:391-394.

McNeil, E. B. and Morse, W. C. (1964), The Institutional Management of Sex in Emotionally Disturbed Children. *Amer. J. Orthopsychiat.*, 34:115-124.

Maier, H. W. (1965), Adolescenthood. *Social Casework*, 46:3-9.

Malmquist, C. P. (1965), Problems of Confidentiality in Child Psychiatry. *Amer. J. Orthopsychiat.*, 35:787-792.

Marcuse, D. J. (1967), The "Army" Incident: The Psychology of Uniforms and Their Abolition on an Adolescent Ward. *Psychiat.*, 30:350-375.

Masterson, J. F. (1956), Prognosis in Adolescent Disorders: Schizophrenia. *J. Nerv. & Ment. Dis.*, 124:219-232.

—— (1967), *The Psychiatric Dilemma of Adolescence.* Little, Brown and Co., Boston.

—— and Washburne, A. (1966), The Symptomatic Adolescent: Psychiatric Illness or Adolescent Turmoil. *Amer. J. Psychiat.*, 122:1240-1248.

Mechanick, P. and Nathan, R. J. (1965), Is Psychiatric Hospitalization Obsolete? *J. Nerv. & Ment. Dis.*, 141:378-383.

Miller, D. (1964), *Growth to Freedom.* London: Tavistock Publications.

Mishler, E. G. and Waxler, N. E. (1966), Family Interaction Processes and Schizophrenia: A Review of Current Theories. *Internat. J. Psychiat.*, 2:375-413.

Moss, P. D. and McEvedy, C. P. (1966), An Epidemic of Overbreathing among School Girls. *Brit. Med. J.*, 2:1295-1300.

Noshpitz, J. D. (1957), Opening Phase in the Psychotherapy of Adolescents with Character Disorders. *Bull. Menn. Clin.*, 21:153-164.

—— (1962), Notes on the Theory of Residential Treatment. *J. Amer. Acad. Child Psychiat.*, 1:284-296.

Offer, D. and Barglow, P. (1960), Adolescent and Young Adult Self-Mutilation Incidents in a General Psychiatric Hospital. *Arch. Gen. Psychiat.* 3:194-204.

——, Sabshin, M., and Marcus, D. (1965), Clinical Evaluation of Normal Adolescents. *Amer. J. Psychiat.*, 121:864-872.

Olsen, T. (1961), Follow-Up Study of Manic-Depressive Patients Whose First Attack Occurred Before the Age of 19. *Acta Psychiat. Scand.*, 37. Suppl. 162, 45-52.

Pitt, R. and Hage, J. (1964), Patterns of Peer Interaction during Adolescence as Prognostic Indicators in Schizophrenia. *Amer. J. Psychiat.*, 120:1089-1096.

Pollack, M., Levenstein, S., and Klein, D. (1968), A Three Year Post Hospital Follow-Up of Adolescent and Adult Schizophrenics. *Amer. J. Orthopsychiat.*, 38:94-109.

Polsky, H. W. (1962), *Cottage Six*. New York: Russell Sage Foundation.

Proctor, J. T. (1958), Hysteria in Childhood. *Amer. J. Orthopsychiat.*, 28:394-407.

Rae-Grant, Q. (1962), Psychopharmacology in Childhood Emotional and Mental Disorders. *J. Pediat.*, 61:626-637.

Redl, F. and Wineman, D. (1957), *The Aggressive Child*. Glencoe, Illinois: Free Press.

Rie, H. E. (1966), Depression in Childhood. *J. Amer. Acad. Child Psychiat.*, 5:653-685.

Rinsley, D. B. (1965), Intensive Psychiatric Hospital Treatment of Adolescents. *Psychiat. Quart.*, 39:405-429.

Robins, E. and O'Neal, P. (1953), Clinical Features of Hysteria in Children with a Note on Prognosis. *Nervous Child*, 10:246-271.

Rosen, J. L. (1963), Personality Factors in the Reactions of Child-Care Workers to Emotionally Disturbed Children. *Psychiat.*, 26:257-265.

Rubenfeld, S. and Stafford, J. W. (1963), An Adolescent Inmate Social System— A Psychosocial Account. *Psychiat.*, 26:241-256.

Rutter, M. and Lockyer, L. (1967), A Five to Fifteen Year Follow-Up Study of Infantile Psychosis. *Brit. J. Psychiat.*, 113:1169-1182.

Safirstein, S. L. (1967), Institutional Transference. *Psychiat. Quart.*, 41:557-566.

Sands, D. E. (1953), A Special Mental Hospital for the Treatment of Psychosis and Neurosis in Juveniles. *J. Ment. Sci.*, 99:123-129.

Seay, B., Alexander, B. K., and Harlow, H. F. (1964), Maternal Behavior of Socially Deprived Rhesus Monkeys. *J. Abnorm. and Soc. Psychol.*, 69:345-354.

Sechehaye, M. A. (1951), *Symbolic Realization*. New York: International Universities Press.

Shader, R. I., Kellam, S. G. and Durell, J. (1967), Social Field Events during the First Week of Hospitalization as Predictors of Treatment Outcome for Psychotic Patients. *J. Nerv. & Ment. Dis.*, 145:142-153.

Shainberg, D. (1966), Personality Restriction in Adolescents. *Psychiat. Quart.*, 40:258-270.

Sobel, R. (1953), The Contributions of Psychoanalysis to the Residential Treatment of Adolescents. In: *Psychoanalysis and Social Work*, ed. P. Heiman. New York: International Universities Press, pp. 242-260.

Spitz, R. (1947), Anaclitic Depression. In: *The Psychoanalytic Study of the Child*, 2:313-342. New York: International Universities Press.

Stahl, A. S. (1960), The First Five Years of the Israel Strauss Adolescent Pavilion Program. *J. Hillside Hosp.*, 9:5-13.

Stearns, A. W. (1955), Accident or Suicide. *J. Maine Med. Assoc.*, 46:313-320.

Stein, W. J. (1967), The Sense of Becoming Psychotic. *Psychiat.*, 30:262-275.

Stierlin, H. (1961), Individual Therapy of Schizophrenic Patients and Hospital Structure. In: *Psychotherapy of the Psychoses*, ed. A. Burton. New York: Basic Books, pp. 329-348.

Toolan, J. T. (1962), Depression in Children and Adolescents. *Amer. J. Orthopsychiat.*, 32:404-415.

Warme, G. E. (1965), Consulting with Aide-Therapists. *Arch. Gen. Psychiat.*, 13:432-438.

Warren, W. (1950), Reactive Psychosis in Adolescence. *J. Ment. Sci.*, 96:448-457.

—— (1952), Inpatient Treatment of Adolescents with Psychological Illness. *Lancet*, 1:147-150.

—— (1965a), A Study of Adolescent Psychiatric In-Patients and the Outcome Six or More Years Later. *J. Child Psychol. and Psychiat.*, 6:1-17.

—— (1965b), Psychiatry of Adolescence. Paper presented at the Royal Medico-Psychological Association Annual Meeting, Edinburgh, May, 1965.

Weakland, J. H. (1960), The "Double Bind" Hypothesis of Schizophrenia and Three Party Interaction. In: *The Etiology of Schizophrenia*, ed. D. D. Jackson, New York: Basic Books, pp. 373-388.

Weiss, M. and Cain, B. (1964), The Residential Treatment of Children and Adolescents with School Phobia. *Amer. J. Orthopsychiat.*, 34:103-114.

Wolpe, J. and Lazarus, A. A. (1966), *Behavior Therapy Techniques*. London: Pergamon.

Worden, F. G. (1951), Psychotherapeutic Aspects of Authority. *Psychiat.*, 14:9-17.

Zusman, J. (1967), Some Explanations of the Changing Appearance of Psychotic Patients, *Internat. J. Psychiat.*, 3:216-247.

Index

245

Berman, A., 50
Beskind, H., 16, 233
Bettelheim, B., 22, 26, 28
Birthdays in hospital, 226
Blackman, N., 187
Boarding homes, 227-228
Body image, 23, 122, 129-130
Boxing, 26, 116, 210
Brody, E. B., 167

Cameron, K., 108
Caplan, L. M., 30, 194
Carek, D. J., 197
Carter, A. B., 200, 218
Character solidification, premature, 140, 148, 160-161, 181, 231, 232-233
Chlordiazepoxide, 133
Chlorpromazine, 123, 127, 132
Christ, A. E., 30, 194
Chwast, J., 142
Clothing, 45-48, 51, 66, 109
    purchase policies, 82
College, 14, 228-229
Communication, nonverbal, 23, 35-52, 56, 66, 98, 108-112, 152-153, 165, 186, 189, 222
Community activities, 54-60, 86-89, 228, 230
    and public school, 27, 56-57, 64, 71, 84
Conscience defects, 185-198
Control
    environmental, see Environment (al)
    parental, 8-12, 163
    staff-patient, 21-22, 83-85, 123, 133, 153, 176-180, 188-189, 211, 218-220
Counts, R. M., 164
Craft, M., 234
Crying, 206
Curran, F. J., 27

Delinquency, 50, 55, 183-198
Depression, 138, 140-149, 200-201, 235
    anaclitic, adolescent, 142-149
    anaclitic, infantile, 142, 146
    endogenous, 141
    reactive, 142
    see also Predepressive states
Developmental arrest, 163-175, 235-236
Dettelbach, M. H., 22
Disorganization, 39, 50
Drugs
    antidepressant, 134-135, 149

emotional effects of, 122-131
    reactions to, 130, 133
    staff attitude toward, 126, 128, 131
    tranquilizing, 20, 129, 132-133, 152, 181
    see also sub specific drug
Durell, J., 54
Dyskinesia, 130

Easson, W. M., 36, 58, 90, 114, 142, 190
Eating patterns, 49, 186, 189
Ego
    mirror-, 180-181, 184, 205
    psychotic, 199-213
Ego deficiency syndrome, 138, 142-149, 161-182, 235-236
Electroconvulsive treatment, 11, 136
Elopement, 41, 46, 72
Empathy in psychotherapy, 98-100, 105-110
Engel, M., 170
Environment (al)
    supportive, 21, 83, 188, 220
    see also Control
Esser, A. H., 49
Exhibitionism, 26

Fairbairn, W. R. D., 172
Family
    as reason for hospitalization, 6
    conflict with patient, 72, 213-218, 230-231
    psychotic, 206-208
Felix, R. H., 3
Fish, B., 123
Freedman, A. M., 200
Friedman, I., 236

Gedo, J. E., 167
Gilbert, A., 3
Glaser, K., 141
Glue-sniffing, 44
Goldsmith, J. M., 197
Granger, C., 234
Greaves, D. C., 98
Greenson, R. R., 167
Grinker, R. R., 2
Group programs
    activity, 17, 108
Gynecomastia, 130

Hage, J., 199

246